Soba noodle–
mushroom soup,
page 57

About WW

WW is a global wellness company and the world's leading commercial weight-management program. We inspire millions of people to adopt healthy habits for real life. Through our engaging digital experience and face-to-face group meetings, members follow our livable and sustainable program that encompasses healthy eating, physical activity, and a positive mindset. With more than five decades of experience in building communities and our deep expertise in behavioral science, we aim to deliver wellness for all. To learn more about the WW approach to healthy living, please visit ww.com. For more information about our global business, visit our corporate website at corporate.ww.com.

**Lemony fennel
and radicchio,
page 137**

Contents

About our recipes

While losing weight isn't only about what you eat, WW realizes the critical role it plays in your success and overall good health. That's why our philosophy is to offer great-tasting, easy recipes that are nutritious as well as delicious. Our recipes emphasize the kinds of healthy foods we love: lots of fresh fruits and vegetables, most of which have 0 SmartPoints value, and lean proteins, some of which have 0 SmartPoints and others that are low in SmartPoints. We also try to ensure that our recipes fall within the recommendations of the U.S. Dietary Guidelines for Americans—lower in saturated fat and sugar with plenty of fruits and vegetables, lean proteins, and low-fat dairy—so they support a diet that promotes health and reduces the risk for disease. If you have special dietary needs, consult with your health-care professional for advice on a diet that is best for you, then adapt these recipes to meet your specific nutritional needs.

Get started, keep going, and enjoy good nutrition

At WW, we believe that eating well makes life better, no matter where you are in your weight-loss journey. These tasty recipes are ideal, whether you're just getting started or have already reached your goals on the SmartPoints system. Unlike other weight-loss programs, which focus solely on calories, the SmartPoints system guides you toward healthier foods that are lower in sugar and saturated fat, and higher in protein. But this isn't a diet—all food is "in." Eating well should be fun, energizing, and delicious, so that healthy food choices become second nature. To get maximum satisfaction, keep the following in mind:

- On the WW Freestyle™ program, eating a mix of foods (rather than all ZeroPoint™ meals) can help you avoid feeling bored or deprived. Remember, there's room for all SmartPoints foods in your plan—variety is key to a healthy and livable eating style.

- SmartPoints values are given for each recipe. The SmartPoints value for each ingredient is assigned based on the number of calories and the amount of saturated fat, sugar, and protein in each ingredient. The SmartPoints values for each ingredient are then added together and divided by the number of servings, and the result is rounded.

- Recipes include approximate nutritional information: They are analyzed for Calories (Cal), Total Fat, Saturated Fat (Sat Fat), Sodium (Sod), Total Carbohydrates (Total Carb), Sugar, Dietary Fiber (Fib), and Protein (Prot). The nutritional values are obtained from the WW database, which is maintained by registered dietitians.

- To boost flavor, we often include fresh herbs or a squeeze of citrus instead of increasing the salt. If you don't need to restrict your sodium intake, feel free to add a touch more salt.

- Look for these symbols throughout the book to choose recipes that fit best with your dietary needs:

  Vegetarian: Recipes that contain no animal flesh foods or products made from animal flesh, though they may contain eggs and dairy products.

  Vegan: Recipes that contain no animal flesh foods, eggs, dairy products, or honey.

  Gluten free: Recipes that contain no wheat, barley, or rye, or any products that are made from these ingredients.

  Dairy free: Recipes that contain no milk from any animal and no products made from animal milk.

  Nut free: Recipes that contain no tree nuts or peanuts.

  Note: Recipes conform to the icon designations, but the "Freestyle it" tip and "Add this" tip serving suggestions may not.

- Recipe introductory headnote suggestions and "Freestyle it" and "Add this" tips have a SmartPoints value of 0 unless otherwise stated.
- For information about the WW plan, please visit ww.com/us/m/cms/plan-basics.

Calculations not what you expected?

SmartPoints values for the recipes in this book are calculated without counting the ZeroPoint foods—fruits, most vegetables, and some lean proteins that are part of the plan. However, the nutritional information does include the nutrient content of these ingredients. This means you may notice discrepancies with the SmartPoints value you calculate using the nutrition information provided for the recipe versus the SmartPoints value listed for the recipe. That's because the SmartPoints values for the recipes that contain ZeroPoint ingredients have been adjusted to reflect those ingredients, while the nutrition information provided includes the nutrition for all of the ingredients. For tracking purposes, use the SmartPoints value listed for the recipe. Also, please note, when fruits and veggies are liquefied or pureed (as in a smoothie), their nutrient content is incorporated into the recipe calculations. These nutrients can increase the SmartPoints.

Alcohol is included in our SmartPoints calculations. Because alcohol information is generally not included on nutrition labels, it's not an option you can include when using the handheld or online SmartPoints calculator or the WW app. But since we include the alcohol information that we get from our database in our recipes, you might notice discrepancies between the SmartPoints you see here in our recipes and the values you get using the calculator. The SmartPoints listed for our recipes are the most accurate values.

Choosing ingredients

As you learn to eat more healthfully and add more wholesome foods to your meals, consider these:

- **Lean meats and poultry**
  Purchase lean meats and poultry, and trim them of all visible fat before cooking. When poultry is cooked with the skin on, we recommend removing the skin before eating. Nutritional information for recipes that include meat, poultry, and fish is based on cooked skinless, boneless portions (unless otherwise stated) with the fat trimmed.

- **Seafood**
  Whenever possible, our recipes call for seafood that is sustainable and deemed the most healthful for human consumption so that your choice of seafood is not only good for the oceans but also good for you. For more information about the best seafood choices and to download a pocket guide, go to the Environmental Defense Fund at seafood.edf.org, the Monterey Bay Aquarium at seafoodwatch.org, or the Safina Center at safinacenter.org.

- **Produce**
  For the best flavor, maximum nutrient content, and the lowest prices, buy fresh, local produce such as vegetables, leafy greens, and fruits in season. Rinse them thoroughly before using, and keep a supply of cut-up vegetables and fruits in your refrigerator for convenient healthy snacks.

- **Whole grains**
  Explore your market for whole-grain products such as whole wheat and whole-grain breads and pastas, brown rice, bulgur, barley, cornmeal, whole wheat couscous, oats, farro, and quinoa to enjoy with your meals.

**Warm roasted
butternut squash salad,
page 68**

WW Freestyle recipes— easier, tastier, and faster with just 5 ingredients

Whether you are a family of four or five or a streamlined family of one or two, getting healthy, well-prepared dishes on the table day after day can be a challenge. But we have the solution—recipes that use up to five ingredients and turn out deliciously tempting dishes.

Here's our secret. When your ingredients are top-notch (that includes our go-to Freestyle ZeroPoint™ ingredients, such as skinless chicken and turkey breast, seafood, some plant-based protein and veggies, eggs, plain fat-free yogurt, and fruits), there's no need to mask or muddle their flavor with unnecessary add-ons.

In the Simply 5 Cookbook, the recipes have been carefully crafted to showcase easy-to-find ingredients in a way that shows them off to their best advantage. We've got you covered, from breakfasts to soups and salads to main dishes, and all manner of greens and grains. There's also a jewel box of a chapter on sweet nothings because they're simply delicious!

Our plan when developing these recipes was simple. Use only five ingredients (oil, cooking spray, water, salt, and pepper are not counted) in a way that makes them shine. Although the recipes cut across the seasons, we recommend taking advantage of seasonal produce whenever possible. Not only do fruits and vegetables taste best in season but they're also a better buy.

Some of the tips suggest optional ingredients, such as an herb, spice, or other flavorful item that will contribute an additional layer of flavor. Take advantage of these suggestions when you have a few extra minutes to spend in the kitchen.

So, what are you waiting for? Dive in and enjoy the Simply 5 Cookbook...you have nothing to lose except time spent in the kitchen and everything to gain when it comes to delicious eating.

The minimalist kitchen

Even with recipes that use only five ingredients and require just a few pieces of equipment, if your kitchen is disorganized it will take more time to cook—and be less enjoyable too. Take a hard look at how your kitchen is set up, then use our tips to turn your workspace around and make you a more efficient cook.

The kitchen set-up

Declutter and organize

- If you can't easily find what you need in your utensil drawer, consider buying a drawer separator to divide it into sections. Give away kitchen equipment you no longer use.

  If you have multiple sets of measuring cups or spoons or duplicate utensils, downsize to the number you actually use when cooking. Toss kitchen gadgets that seemed clever when you bought them—that garlic slicer or kale stem stripper—but now collect dust. Donate the excess to a local thrift shop or school.

- Park seldom-used equipment on a top shelf. If your kitchen space is limited, store items in another room or put them into covered plastic containers and store in your garage or basement. This is especially good for seasonal items such as Christmas cookie cutters, specialty cake pans, and very large pots.

- Make cooking more convenient. Many of the recipes in this book use only one pot, skillet, roasting pan, or baking sheet. Store the ones you use most often in a lower cabinet as close to the stove as possible. Put a nesting set of bowls and your cutting boards near where you prep. Place your go-to whisks, ladles, spatulas, and wooden spoons in a jar on your counter for easy reach. Keep knives safe and sharp by using a knife block or in-drawer slotted knife organizer.

Streamline your pantry

- Save space by eliminating tempting foods like cookies and chips to make room for healthier fare. The same goes for unwanted food gifts or condiments you thought you would like but didn't. Donate unwanted, unopened, unexpired items to a local food bank or give to friends or neighbors.

- Organize your pantry by zones. Store like things, such as canned broths, beans, tomatoes, salsas, rice, and whole grains together. Place frequently used items, such as oil, vinegar, pastas, and canned broths front and center on a shelf. Put items you use less often on upper or lower shelves.

- Put the dried herbs and spices you use most often along with salt and pepper in a basket, in a drawer, or on a shelf near your food prep area. You will be amazed at how much time this will save. Alphabetize the remaining herb and spice bottles to make them easy to spot. And while you're at it, toss dried herbs and spices you've had more than two years and only replenish those you use.

How to stock a basic healthy pantry

Keep these foods on hand and make cooking our 5-ingredient dishes even easier and faster.

Pantry

☐ Artichoke hearts, canned

☐ Bacon, fully cooked, ready to serve

☐ Baking potatoes, microwave-ready

☐ Beans, canned (assorted)

☐ Broth (chicken, beef, vegetable)

☐ Chopped nuts (assorted)

☐ Coconut, shredded

☐ Cranberry sauce, canned

☐ Dried bread crumbs (plain, seasoned)

☐ Green chiles, mild, canned

☐ Instant espresso powder

☐ Grains, quick-cook packaged grains (farro, barley)

☐ Marinara/tomato sauce

☐ Pastes (tomato and anchovy), refrigerate upon opening

☐ Peanut butter

☐ Rice, boil-in-bag (white, brown)

☐ Rice, fully cooked (white, brown)

Fridge

☐ Baby lettuce, pre-washed (assorted)

☐ Baby spinach, bagged

☐ Beets, fully cooked, vacuum-packed

☐ Broccoli crumbles

☐ Brussels sprouts, shredded

☐ Butternut squash, peeled and diced

☐ Carrots, shredded/matchstick

☐ Cauliflower crumbles ("rice")

☐ Cheese, shredded and grated

☐ Chicken, rotisserie

☐ Coleslaw, broccoli slaw

☐ Edamame, shelled, fully-cooked

☐ Eggs, hard-cooked

☐ Garlic cloves, peeled

☐ Garlic, chopped

☐ Garlic, ginger, basil, lemongrass, and chile refrigerated pastes

☐ Hummus

☐ Lentils, fully cooked, vacuum-packed

☐ Mushrooms, sliced

☐ Pesto, basil

Freezer

☐ Bell peppers, chopped

☐ Berries, unsweetened (various)

☐ Corn, kernels

☐ Edamame, shelled

☐ Mango, chunks, unsweetened

☐ Onion, chopped

☐ Pearl onions, peeled

☐ Pizza dough (plain, whole wheat)

☐ Spinach, chopped

☐ Waffles and pancakes, whole grain/whole wheat

☐ Whole grains, fully cooked (farro, quinoa, wheat berries, rice)

Global glossary

Travel no farther than your supermarket to enjoy these flavorful ingredients.

Bean thread noodles
These noodles are also called cellophane noodles, Chinese vermicelli, and glass noodles. Thin and translucent, they are made from mung bean starch. Bean thread noodles are cooked by being briefly soaked in very hot water until softened, then drained.

Chickpea flour
This flour is made from ground dried chickpeas. It is gluten free, high in protein, and a staple ingredient in many cuisines. In Nice, France, it is turned into tasty pancakes known as socca that are enjoyed as a snack and cooked into a silky smooth soup (see recipe, page 50).

Chili-garlic sauce
Chili-garlic sauce is a piquant blend of coarsely ground fresh chiles, garlic, vinegar, and salt. It can be used as a condiment or added to cooked dishes, marinades, and sauces. Just a touch is enough to contribute bold flavor.

Chili oil
This vegetable oil has been infused with chile peppers that turn it a deep orange-red. It is a staple ingredient in Chinese, Asian, and Southeast Asian cooking and is found in the Asian food aisle in supermarkets.

Coconut oil
Coconut oil is mechanically—not chemically—pressed from the meat of mature coconuts. It is solid at room temperature but quickly melts when heated. This oil is used in both sweet and savory dishes and is a favorite of vegans because of its rich flavor.

Crème fraîche
The term for *fresh cream* in French, crème fraiche is thickened heavy cream that is slightly tangy from the addition of buttermilk, sour cream, or plain yogurt. It is often used in place of whipped cream and is served alongside tarte tatin (upside-down apple tart), as well as soups and smoked salmon appetizers.

Fermented black beans,
Fermented black beans, also known as salted black beans, are made from black soybeans that have been salted and fermented, which gives them their rich, deep flavor. They are sold in small plastic bags in Asian markets and are inexpensive. Fermented black beans are usually briefly soaked in water then minced or mashed with a mortar and pestle before being added to stir-fries. A little goes a long way, so a tablespoon or two is all that is needed.

Fish sauce
Known as nam pla in Thailand and nuoc mam in Vietnam, this pungent amber-colored fermented sauce adds rich complexity to dishes. The best-quality fish sauce contains only water, anchovies and salt. It is always used judiciously, so a bottle lasts a long time.

Hoisin sauce
This is a thick, dark, pungent sauce made from soybean paste, chiles, and salt and can also contain sugar, vinegar, and garlic. It is often added to Chinese barbecue sauces and glazes. Lee Kum Kee is a popular brand available in supermarkets.

Kecap manis
Used in Indonesian cooking, this is a type of soy sauce made by fermenting soybeans with salt and palm sugar. Star anise and garlic are also sometimes added for a more complex flavor. Kecap manis is thick and dark and reminiscent of molasses. It is best added judiciously.

Kimchee
Kimchee is a traditional Korean side dish with a 3,000-year history. It is made from chile-laced Napa cabbage that has been fermented in crocks. It can be served on its own or added to fried rice or other dishes. Kimchee is so revered that there is a kimchee museum in Seoul, South Korea. It can be found in specialty food stores, online, and in large supermarkets.

Lemongrass
This tropical plant is widely used in Asian cooking. It has a

delicate citrus-floral flavor and is available fresh, frozen, as a fresh paste, and dried (not recommended). Look for firm, light green stalks, and refrigerate tightly wrapped in plastic wrap for up to 2 weeks or in the freezer for up to 6 months. To prepare, cut off the dry end of the stalk and the papery top. Make a slit down the length of the stalk and peel off the tough outer layers to reach the pale, tender core. Smash it with the side of a large knife to release its oils and finely chop.

Mascarpone
A soft, creamy, mild triple cream–style Italian cheese, mascarpone is made from heavy cream. Sold in small containers in most supermarkets, it is best known as an ingredient in tiramisu.

Mirin
This sweet Japanese rice wine is used to lend a bit of acidity to dishes. Dry sherry and sweet Marsala wine make fine substitutes.

Miso
Miso is fermented soybean paste. There are three types: white, yellow, and red. White miso is made of soybeans and rice and is fermented for a short period of time, which makes it mild. It is best used in dressings, soups, and marinades. Yellow miso is made

continues on next page

How to add a quick flavor boost
Let these exotics give a dash of wow to everyday dishes.

Aleppo pepper
(dried pepper flakes that offer heat, complex flavor, and bright acidity)
Store: up to 1 year in pantry
Try in: rubs, marinades, kebabs, grilled meat, pasta and rice dishes, sauces, stews, lentils, brownies, spiced nuts

Garam masala
(a mix of cardamom, cinnamon, cloves, coriander, cumin, black pepper, star anise, and turmeric)
Store: up to 1 year in pantry
Try in: rubs, marinades, curries, stews, braises

Harissa
(very hot seasoning paste from Tunisia sold in small cans and tubes)
Store: up to 1 year in refrigerator
Try in: marinades for grilled meat or fish, roasted vegetables, soups and stews, couscous, rice dishes

Horseradish
(member of mustard family, this root is prized for its ability to add a wallop of heat when freshly grated)
Store: bottled horseradish up to 2 months in refrigerator; fresh horseradish up to 2 weeks in crisper drawer
Try in: Bloody Mary mix, dips, beets, meat loaf

Sriracha
(hot sauce made from blend of chile peppers, vinegar, garlic, sugar, and salt)
Store: up to 1 year in refrigerator
Try in: any dish to add complex heat

Sumac
(slightly moist, coarse-grained dark powder with fruity, tangy aroma and slightly salty aftertaste)
Store: up to 1 year in pantry
Try in: potatoes, tomatoes, winter squash, onion, eggplant, zucchini, yogurt

Vadouvan
(French-style curry powder that contains shallots or onions; sweet with touch of smokiness)
Store: up to 1 year in pantry
Try in: popcorn, dips, chocolate baked goods, vinaigrettes, rubs, marinades, vegetables, yogurt, grains, meat, chicken

with fermented soybeans and barley, which lend it a stronger taste. It is best used in hearty dressings, soups, bold marinades, and glazes. Red miso, the saltiest and most pungent variety, is made from soybeans and barley and is aged for a longer period of time. It is best used in braises and with vegetables.

Naan
A leavened flatbread from India, naan is made from flour, yogurt, salt, and yeast. Traditionally the dough is slapped against the wall of a tandoor oven until flattened then baked over a wood fire. It is best enjoyed brushed with ghee (clarified butter). Stonefire Authentic Flatbreads is a brand of naan available in supermarkets.

Oyster sauce
Oyster sauce is a rich concentrated blend of oyster, soy sauce, sugar, and salt that is thickened with cornstarch. This brown sauce is strongly flavored so is best used sparingly in cooked dishes such as stir-fries. It is commonly used in Cantonese, Thai, and Vietnamese cooking.

Pancetta
This Italian-style bacon is salt cured but not smoked. It is found in specialty food stores where it is sliced to order. You can also find it diced in small containers alongside the pre-sliced cold cuts.

Parmigiano-Reggiano
The only authentic Parmesan cheese is Parmegiano-Reggiano. It is made from cow's milk and is aged for at least 2 years in specially designated areas in Italy. It has a rich, sharp flavor and a creamy, granular texture. Look for a yellow rind with the words Parmigiano-Reggiano stamped. Refrigerate double wrapped in wax paper and a zip-close plastic bag to keep it fresh.

Pecorino-Romano
This is a hard, pungent sheep's milk cheese from Italy. Due to its saltier nature, it should be added judiciously to dishes where a bit of salty, cheesy punch is a welcome addition.

Pepperoncini
These brined sweet peppers are medium hot. They make a great addition to sandwiches, antipasto platters, and Greek salads.

Prosciutto
An Italian dry-cured ham, prosciutto is served very thinly sliced. It has a sweet, meaty, buttery flavor and is produced in several regions in Italy. Prosciutto de Parma is the mildest and sweetest variety of prosciutto and is a bit pricier. Prosciutto is sold in specialty food stores, where it is sliced to order and presliced in supermarkets.

Rice stick noodles
These noodles are made from rice flour and water. They are available in thin, medium, and wide widths. Rice noodles are cooked in boiling water until softened before being added to dishes. Wide rice noodles are best known for their use in pad Thai, a noodle dish from Thailand.

Ricotta salata
This cheese is made from ricotta cheese. Ricotta means "re-cooked" and salata means "salted." To make ricotta salata, fresh ricotta cheese is pressed, salted, and aged for a minimum of 90 days. Ricotta salata, which resembles feta cheese, is most often used in salads and is ideal for shredding and slicing.

Sambal oelek
This Indonesian ground chile paste is used to add pure heat to dishes. One of the most popular brands in the U.S. is Huy Fong, the California-based company that also produces Sriracha.

Thai curry paste
Thai curry paste is available both red and green. Green curry paste, which is quite hot, is made from a mix of green chiles, lemongrass, garlic, shrimp paste, kaffir lime leaves, and salt. Red curry paste is a blend of red chiles and spices and has a medium level of heat.

Tomato and garlic-stuffed peppers, page 144

Chapter 1
Rise and shine

Gruyère and asparagus frittata

Gruyère and asparagus frittata

Serves 4

Buttery, nutty Gruyère (groo-YEHR) cheese is the perfect partner for the asparagus in this elegant yet easy frittata. This delectable cheese is named for a valley of the same name in Switzerland.

2	**teaspoons olive oil**
10	**asparagus spears, trimmed and cut into 1-inch pieces**
1	**large shallot, minced**
5	**large eggs**
1	**tablespoon water**
½	**teaspoon salt**
¼	**teaspoon black pepper**
¼	**cup shredded Gruyère or Swiss cheese**

1 Preheat broiler.

2 Heat oil in 10-inch ovenproof skillet over medium-high heat. Add asparagus and shallot and cook, stirring frequently, until vegetables have softened, about 4 minutes.

3 Meanwhile, beat eggs, water, salt, and pepper in medium bowl; stir in Gruyère. Pour egg mixture over asparagus, gently stirring until combined. Reduce heat to medium and cook, covered, until eggs have set in center, about 5 minutes.

4 Place frittata under broiler 5 inches from heat source and broil until lightly browned, about 1 minute. Let frittata stand about 2 minutes before cutting into wedges.

3 **SmartPoints value per serving** (¼ of frittata): 185 Cal, 13 g Total Fat, 5 g Sat Fat, 482 mg Sod, 4 g Total Carb, 2 g Sugar, 1 g Fib, 13 g Prot.

Overstuffed western omelette

Serves 2

Brimming with onion, bell pepper, and diced ham, this diner egg dish is also called a Denver omelette. Unlike the classic French version, where the filling is enclosed in the eggs, here the eggs are poured over the filling and it all gets cooked together.

2	teaspoons canola oil
½	cup diced red bell pepper
½	cup diced green bell pepper
2	scallions, thinly sliced
¼	pound low-sodium ham, diced
¼	teaspoon salt
⅛	teaspoon black pepper
4	large eggs, lightly beaten

1 Heat oil in medium nonstick skillet over medium heat. Add red and green bell peppers, scallions, ham, salt, and black pepper and cook, stirring, until vegetables have softened, about 5 minutes.

2 Pour eggs over vegetable mixture and cook until eggs are almost set, about 2 minutes, gently lifting edge of eggs with silicone spatula to allow uncooked portion of egg to run underneath. Fold omelette in half and cook until set, about 1 minute longer. Cut omelette in half and place one portion on each of 2 plates.

3 **SmartPoints value per serving** (½ of omelette): 285 Cal, 17 g Total Fat, 4 g Sat Fat, 979 mg Sod, 6 g Total Carb, 2 g Sugar, 2 g Fib, 25 g Prot.

Add this

Our western omelette is a classic, but to make it heartier, add ½ cup of packaged diced cooked potatoes (found in the produce section of supermarkets) to the skillet along with the bell peppers in step 1. This will increase the per-serving SmartPoints by 2.

Broccoli-egg strudel

Serves 6

2 **cups small broccoli florets**
10 **(9 x 14-inch) sheets phyllo dough, thawed if frozen**
4 **large eggs**
½ **teaspoon salt**
¼ **teaspoon black pepper**
2 **teaspoons olive oil**
½ **cup shredded reduced-fat Jarlsberg cheese**

1 Preheat oven to 375°F. Spray rimmed baking sheet with nonstick spray.

2 Meanwhile, bring medium saucepan of water to boil. Add broccoli and cook until crisp-tender, about 3 minutes. Drain and pat dry with paper towels. Set aside.

3 Lay 1 phyllo sheet on work surface with long side facing you. (Keep remaining phyllo covered with damp kitchen towel and plastic wrap to prevent it from drying out.) Lightly spray phyllo with nonstick spray. Layer 9 more phyllo sheets on top, lightly spraying each sheet. Cover with plastic wrap.

4 Beat eggs, salt, and pepper in medium bowl. Stir in broccoli.

5 Heat oil in medium nonstick skillet over medium heat. Add egg mixture and cook, stirring with silicone spatula, just until set. about 2 minutes. Spoon broccoli-egg mixture over phyllo, leaving 2-inch border. Sprinkle with Jarlsberg.

6 Fold short sides of phyllo over filling, then gently roll up jelly-roll style. Place strudel, seam-side down, on prepared baking sheet and lightly spray with nonstick spray. Cut four 1-inch slits in top of strudel to allow steam to escape. Bake until filling is heated through and phyllo is golden, about 20 minutes. Let strudel cool on baking sheet on wire rack 15 minutes. Cut into 6 slices.

4 **SmartPoints value per serving** (1 slice): 185 Cal, 8 g Total Fat, 2 g Sat Fat, 485 mg Sod, 19 g Total Carb, 1 g Sugar, 1 g Fib, 9 g Prot.

Zucchini and
goat cheese
omelette

Zucchini and goat cheese omelette

Serves 1

2	teaspoons olive oil
1	small zucchini, cut into matchstick strips
2	large egg whites
1	large egg
¼	teaspoon salt
⅛	teaspoon black pepper
2	tablespoons crumbled soft goat cheese
4	fresh basil leaves, thinly sliced

1 Heat 1 teaspoon of oil in small nonstick skillet over medium heat. Add zucchini and cook, stirring, until crisp-tender, about 2 minutes. Transfer to small bowl and set aside.

2 Whisk together egg whites, egg, salt, and pepper in small bowl.

3 Heat remaining 1 teaspoon oil in same skillet (no need to wash skillet) over medium heat. Pour egg mixture into skillet and tilt so eggs cover bottom of skillet. Cook, without stirring, until bottom of egg mixture is almost set, about 2 minutes.

4 Spoon zucchini onto one half of eggs and sprinkle with goat cheese and basil. Fold unfilled portion of eggs over filling to enclose. Cook until omelette is set, about 1 minute longer.

6 **SmartPoints value per serving** (1 omelette): 287 Cal, 21 g Total Fat, 7 g Sat Fat, 911 mg Sod, 5 g Total Carb, 4 g Sugar, 1 g Fib, 21 g Prot.

Baked eggs in tomatoes florentine

Serves 4

The most efficient way to hollow out a tomato is with a grapefruit knife. It has an angled tip and a blade that is serrated on both sides.

4   (½-pound) ripe tomatoes
½   teaspoon table salt
2   tablespoons grated Parmesan cheese
1   tablespoon Italian-seasoned dried bread crumbs
2   teaspoons olive oil
1   (5-ounce) container baby spinach
¼   teaspoon black pepper plus additional for serving
4   large eggs
Large pinch coarse sea salt, such as Maldon

1 Preheat oven to 400°F. Line medium baking sheet with sheet of parchment paper.

2 Meanwhile, with small serrated knife, cut ½-inch slice off top of each tomato and discard. With grapefruit knife or same serrated knife, carefully cut around inside of each tomato to remove fleshy center. With spoon, scoop out juicy pulp with seeds and press through small sieve set over cup. Measure out ¼ cup tomato water and reserve. Discard any remaining tomato water and seeds. Sprinkle tomato shells with ¼ teaspoon of table salt.

3 Mix together Parmesan and bread crumbs in cup.

4 Heat oil in large skillet over medium heat. Add spinach, remaining ¼ teaspoon table salt, ¼ teaspoon of pepper, and reserved tomato water. Cook, stirring, until spinach is wilted and tomato water has evaporated, about 3 minutes. Stir in Parmesan-crumb mixture.

5 Place tomatoes on prepared baking sheet and bake 6 minutes. Spoon spinach mixture into tomatoes, dividing evenly. Use back of spoon to line tomato shells with spinach, leaving centers empty. Crack 1 egg into cup and slip into tomato. Repeat.

6 Cover tomatoes with sheet of nonstick foil and bake 10 minutes. Uncover and bake until tomatoes are tender, egg whites have set, and yolks are slightly runny, about 10 minutes longer. Sprinkle pepper and coarse salt over each egg and serve.

2 **SmartPoints value per serving** (1 stuffed tomato): 161 Cal, 9 g Total Fat, 2 g Sat Fat, 543 mg Sod, 12 g Total Carb, 6 g Sugar, 4 g Fib, 10 g Prot.

Baked eggs in tomatoes florentine

Greek-style
breakfast pitas

Greek-style breakfast pitas

Serves 2

Not planning a trip to Greece anytime soon? Don't despair. Enjoy some typical Greek ingredients by whipping up this easy breakfast pita sandwich. Add ¼ teaspoon of dried Greek seasoning and 2–3 teaspoons of chopped fresh oregano, if you like.

3	**large eggs**
¼	**cup crumbled reduced-fat feta cheese**
¼	**teaspoon black pepper**
⅛	**teaspoon salt**
1	**cup tightly packed baby spinach**
½	**cup grape or cherry tomatoes, halved**
1	**large whole wheat pita bread, halved and toasted**

1 Beat eggs in small bowl. Stir in feta, pepper, and salt.

2 Spray medium heavy skillet with nonstick spray and set over medium-high heat. Add spinach and cook, stirring occasionally, until wilted, about 2 minutes.

3 Reduce heat to medium. Add egg mixture and tomatoes and cook, stirring frequently, until eggs are just set, about 1½ minutes. Spoon egg-tomato mixture evenly into pita halves.

3 **SmartPoints value per serving** (¾ cup egg mixture and ½ pita): 226 Cal, 10 g Total Fat, 4 g Sat Fat, 600 mg Sod, 19 g Total Carb, 2 g Sugar, 3 g Fib, 16 g Prot.

Skinny breakfast sausages and eggs

Serves 4

½ **pound ground turkey (7% fat or less)**

2–3 **teaspoons finely chopped fresh sage or 1 teaspoon dried**

1 **teaspoon finely chopped fresh thyme**

¼ **teaspoon salt, or to taste**

¼ **teaspoon black pepper**

4 **large eggs, poached, scrambled, or fried**

1 Combine turkey, sage, thyme, salt, and pepper in large bowl. Using fork, gently mix until seasonings are evenly incorporated but not overmixed.

2 Place sheet of parchment paper or nonstick foil on work surface. Divide turkey mixture into 8 equal portions and place on parchment, using about 2 tablespoons turkey mixture for each. With damp hands, shape into 2½-inch round patties (don't worry if edges look craggy or have cracks).

3 Generously spray large nonstick skillet with nonstick spray and set over medium heat. Place patties in skillet and cook until sausages are lightly browned and just cooked through, about 2 minutes per side. Serve with eggs of choice.

2 **SmartPoints value per serving** (2 sausage patties and 1 egg): 160 Cal, 10 g Total Fat, 3 g Sat Fat, 256 mg Sod, 1 g Total Carb, 0 g Sugar, 0 g Fib, 17 g Prot.

Bacon and Cheddar-coddled eggs

Serves 4

Wouldn't recognize a coddled egg if you saw one? It's simply eggs cooked gently in custard cups or lidded ceramic coddling cups, usually in a hot water bath. Brits love their coddled eggs served with crisp toast "fingers" for dunking into the yolks.

½ **cup thawed frozen chopped spinach, squeezed dry**

4 **large eggs**

¼ **teaspoon black pepper**

⅛ **teaspoon salt**

4 **slices packaged fully cooked bacon, broken into pieces or chopped**

¼ **cup shredded reduced-fat Cheddar or Swiss cheese**

1 Preheat oven to 350°F. Spray 4 (8-ounce) custard cups or ramekins with nonstick spray; place on small rimmed baking sheet.

2 Divide spinach evenly among prepared custard cups. Beat eggs, pepper, and salt in medium bowl; pour into cups dividing evenly. Top with bacon and sprinkle each with 1 tablespoon Cheddar. Bake until eggs are just set, about 20 minutes.

3 **SmartPoints value per serving** (1 coddled egg): 165 Cal, 11 g Total Fat, 5 g Sat Fat, 403 mg Sod, 2 g Total Carb, 0 g Sugar, 1 g Fib, 14 g Prot.

Cheddar grits with bacon and kale

Serves 4

The key to creamy, lump-free grits is slowly adding the grits while constantly whisking. Once all the grits are added, it's just a matter of cooking them until they are thickened.

4	cups water
1	cup quick-cooking grits
3	cups lightly packed torn kale
2	teaspoons Cajun seasoning
¼	teaspoon salt
4	(¾-ounce) slices Canadian bacon, diced
½	cup shredded reduced-fat Cheddar cheese

1 Bring water to boil in medium saucepan. Slowly whisk in grits. Reduce heat to medium-low and cook, stirring occasionally, until grits have thickened, about 5 minutes. Remove saucepan from heat and cover to keep warm.

2 Meanwhile, heat large skillet over medium-high heat. Add kale and spray with olive oil nonstick spray, tossing until coated. Cook, stirring frequently, until kale is wilted and any liquid has evaporated, about 2 minutes. Stir in Cajun seasoning and salt.

3 Push kale to one side of pan. Add Canadian bacon and cook, stirring once or twice, until heated through, about 1 minute.

4 Spoon grits evenly into 4 bowls. Top evenly with kale-bacon mixture and sprinkle each serving with 2 tablespoons Cheddar.

 SmartPoints value per serving (1¼ cups): 260 Cal, 7g Total Fat, 4 g Sat Fat, 1,110 mg Sod, 33 g Total Carb, 1 g Sugar, 2 g Fib, 15 g Prot.

Freestyle it

Start your meal with a fresh citrus salad of grapefruit and orange segments sprinkled with thinly sliced fresh mint and pomegranate arils, which can be found fresh and frozen, all for 0 SmartPoints.

**Cheddar grits with
bacon and kale**

Chilaquiles bake

Serves 4

This classic Mexican dish is comfort food at its best and a great way to use up leftover tortillas. To make it even tastier, chilaquiles is usually served with a side of refried beans or nopalitos (diced cactus leaves).

⅓   **cup canned black beans, rinsed and drained**

1   **(6-inch) corn tortilla, cut in half and then crosswise into thin strips**

⅓   **cup shredded reduced-fat pepper Jack cheese**

6   **large eggs**

⅓   **cup plus ¼ cup fat-free salsa verde**

1 Preheat oven to 350°F. Spray 4 (6-ounce) custard cups or ramekins with nonstick spray.

2 Divide beans, tortilla strips, and pepper Jack cheese evenly among prepared custard cups. Lightly beat eggs in medium bowl. Stir in ⅓ cup of salsa. Pour egg mixture evenly into cups and place on small rimmed baking sheet. Bake until eggs are just set in center, about 30 minutes. Serve with remaining ¼ cup salsa.

1 **SmartPoints value per serving** (1 custard cup): 180 Cal, 9 g Total Fat, 4 g Sat Fat, 414 mg Sod, 10 g Total Carb, 2 g Sugar, 2 g Fib, 14 g Prot.

Add this

Make this classic Tex-Mex breakfast dish even more delish by topping each serving with a 2-tablespoon dollop of light sour cream, which will up the SmartPoints by 2. While you're at it, sprinkle the dish with coarsely chopped fresh cilantro and thinly sliced rings of jalapeño.

Savory steel-cut oats with kale

Serves 4

We used Quaker oats in this recipe. If you use a different brand, keep in mind that the amount of water and the cooking time may be different than what is stated in the recipe.

4   **scallions, sliced**
1   **garlic clove, thinly sliced**
1   **cup steel-cut oats**
3   **cups water**
¾   **teaspoon salt**
1   **cup thawed frozen chopped kale**
¼   **teaspoon black pepper**
4   **slices turkey bacon, crisp-cooked and torn into small pieces**

1 Spray medium saucepan with olive oil nonstick spray and set over medium heat. Add scallions and garlic and cook, stirring occasionally, until softened, about 3 minutes.

2 Add oats, water, and salt to scallion mixture and bring to boil. Reduce heat and simmer, covered, 15 minutes. Stir in kale and pepper and cook, covered, until oats have softened and most of water is absorbed, about 15 minutes longer.

3 Divide oat mixture evenly among 4 bowls and sprinkle with bacon.

 SmartPoints value per serving (1 cup oat mixture and 1 slice bacon): 194 Cal, 5 g Total Fat, 1 g Sat Fat, 612 mg Sod, 30 g Total Carb, 1 g Sugar, 5 g Fib, 8 g Prot.

Freestyle it
Feeling extra hungry? For 0 SmartPoints you can top each serving of oats with a poached egg. Try it with a few shakes of your favorite hot sauce.

Tropical oats with chia seeds

Serves 4

In this tropics-inspired dish, coconut water infuses subtle flavor into oatmeal.
Each serving is topped with juicy fresh pineapple pieces and crisp coconut chips.
Chia seeds, on trend as well as good for you, make an appearance here as well.

2	**cups pure coconut water**
1	**cup quick-cooking oats**
2	**tablespoons chia seeds**
2	**cups diced fresh pineapple and/or kiwifruit**
¼	**cup toasted sweetened coconut chips**

1 Bring coconut water to boil in medium saucepan; add oats and chia seeds. Reduce heat and simmer, stirring occasionally, until oats are cooked and mixture has thickened, about 5 minutes.

2 Spoon oat mixture evenly into 4 bowls. Top evenly with fruit and coconut chips.

5 **SmartPoints value per serving** (½ cup oat mixture, ½ cup fruit, and 1 tablespoon coconut): 186 Cal, 5 g Total Fat, 2 g Sat Fat, 136 mg Sod, 33 g Total Carb, 13 g Sugar, 7 g Fib, 5 g Prot.

**Tropical oats
with chia seeds**

Maple breakfast pudding

Serves 4

How about serving a steaming cup of frothy cappuccino sprinkled with ground cinnamon with this luscious early meal? Guaranteed to get your day off to a good start, an 8-ounce cap prepared with fat-free milk will add a mere 2 SmartPoints.

2½ **cups plain unsweetened soy milk**

¾ **cup long-grain brown rice**

¼ **cup raisins or dried cranberries**

1 **tablespoon maple syrup**

¾ **teaspoon ground cinnamon**

¼ **teaspoon salt**

1 Bring soy milk to boil in medium saucepan over medium-high heat. Stir in rice, raisins, maple syrup, cinnamon, and salt. Return to boil. Reduce heat to low and cook, covered, until rice is tender and milk is almost absorbed, about 45 minutes.

2 Remove saucepan from heat and let stand 10 minutes before serving.

7 **SmartPoints value per serving** (⅔ cup): 223 Cal, 4 g Total Fat, 1 g Sat Fat, 207 mg Sod, 40 g Total Carb, 9 g Sugar, 3 g Fib, 8 g Prot.

Polenta with brown sugar ricotta

Serves 4

Instant polenta is what makes this recipe a snap to prepare. Even though it cooks in just minutes, the polenta is still a whole grain and a great way to start your day right.

1	**cup low-fat (1%) milk**
1	**cup water**
⅛	**teaspoon salt**
⅔	**cup part-skim ricotta cheese**
1	**tablespoon light brown sugar**
½	**teaspoon vanilla extract**
½	**cup instant polenta**

1 Combine milk, water, and salt in medium saucepan and bring to boil over medium-high heat.

2 Meanwhile, combine ricotta, brown sugar, and vanilla in food processor and process until smooth. Set aside.

3 Slowly add polenta to milk-water mixture in thin, steady stream, whisking constantly. Cook, stirring constantly, until polenta has thickened and is creamy, 3–5 minutes. Divide polenta evenly among 4 bowls and top evenly with ricotta mixture.

(5) **SmartPoints value per serving** (⅔ cup): 161 Cal, 4 g Total Fat, 2 g Sat Fat, 142 mg Sod, 22 g Total Carb, 5 g Sugar, 2 g Fib, 8 g Prot.

Add this

Our polenta-ricotta dish is truly satisfying as is, but you can sprinkle the polenta with finely grated lemon or orange zest or ground cinnamon for another layer of flavor.

Red, white, and blue parfaits

Red, white, and blue parfaits

Serves 4

2   cups plain low-fat yogurt
2   tablespoons chia seeds
½   teaspoon grated lemon zest
2   cups mixed berries
    (raspberries, blueberries
    and sliced strawberries)
½   cup low-fat granola

1 Combine yogurt, chia seeds, and lemon zest in medium bowl. Cover and refrigerate until chia seeds have softened, at least 4 hours or up to overnight.

2 Spoon ½ cup yogurt mixture into each of 4 mason jars or glasses. Top each with ½ cup berries and 2 tablespoons granola.

5   **SmartPoints value per serving** (generous 1 cup): 186 Cal, 4 g Total Fat, 2 g Sat Fat, 118 mg Sod, 30 g Total Carb, 17 g Sugar, 5 g Fib, 9 g Prot.

Chapter 2
Opening act

Gin-basil smash

Gin-basil smash

Serves 6

Muddle, don't mash! With a muddler, which resembles a wooden pestle, or with a wooden spoon, lightly crush the basil leaves, giving the muddler a few gentle twists as you go. When the basil aroma wafts into the air, you're done.

⅓ **cup lightly packed Thai, lemon, or regular basil leaves plus leaves for garnish**

1 **cup gin**

½ **cup lemon juice**

3–4 **tablespoons light agave nectar**

1 **cup ice cubes plus additional for serving**

1 Put basil into cocktail shaker and gently muddle with muddler or wooden spoon.

2 Add all remaining ingredients to shaker; cover and shake vigorously until outside of shaker looks icy.

3 Strain gin mixture into 4 ice-filled small wineglasses. Garnish with basil leaves.

 SmartPoints value per serving (about ⅓ cup without ice): 96 Cal, 0 g Total Fat, 0 g Sat Fat, 1 mg Sod, 3 g Total Carb, 2 g Sugar, 0 g Fib, 0 g Prot.

Freestyle it
Turn this drink into a spritzer by topping off each serving with seltzer for 0 SmartPoints.

Watermelon mojitos

Serves 6

The mojito, a world-famous Cuban cocktail, has been around since the early 20th century. While it's traditionally made with rum, we found that fresh watermelon pairs better with vodka, which is more lightly flavored.

⅓ **cup lightly packed fresh mint leaves**

6 **cups tightly packed 1½-inch watermelon chunks**

1 **cup vodka**

¼ **cup lime juice**

1 **tablespoon light agave nectar or to taste**

Ice cubes

Watermelon spears, thinly sliced lime, and/or fresh mint sprigs

1 Put mint into pitcher and gently muddle with muddler or wooden spoon.

2 Put watermelon into blender and blend on low speed until smooth. Pour puree through fine-mesh sieve set over medium bowl, pressing hard on solids to extract all liquid; discard solids. Skim off foam from watermelon juice and discard.

3 Add watermelon juice to pitcher and stir in vodka, lime juice, and agave. Pour into 6 ice-filled glasses. Garnish with watermelon spears, lime slices, and/or mint sprigs.

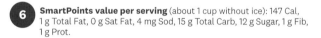

6 **SmartPoints value per serving** (about 1 cup without ice): 147 Cal, 1 g Total Fat, 0 g Sat Fat, 4 mg Sod, 15 g Total Carb, 12 g Sugar, 1 g Fib, 1 g Prot.

Mango-coconut agua fresca

Serves 8

To cut and pit a mango, stand it on a long side, hold a sharp knife slightly off center, and carefully slice through the flesh, cutting off an oval "steak" of mango to separate it from the pit. Repeat on the other side.

4   **cups pure coconut water, preferably with pulp**

2   **ripe mangoes, peeled, pitted, and cubed (about 3 cups)**

3–4 tablespoons lime juice

Ice-cold water

Ice cubes

Lime wedges

1 Combine coconut water and mango in blender and blend until smooth. Stir in lime juice and add enough ice-cold water to equal 8 cups.

2 Pour into 8 ice-filled glasses and garnish with lime wedges.

4 **SmartPoints value per serving** (1 cup without ice): 65 Cal, 0 g Total Fat, 0 g Sat Fat, 37 mg Sod, 17 g Total Carb, 14 g Sugar, 1 g Fib, 1 g Prot.

Coconut-cucumber splash

Coconut-cucumber splash

Serves 4

This is the perfect time to take advantage of spearmint growing in your garden or window-box container. Add a tangle of fragrant mint sprigs to this refresher for another layer of summertime flavor.

1 **(33½-ounce) carton coconut water, chilled**

1 **mini cucumber, thinly sliced on diagonal**

Juice of 1 lime

1 **tablespoon light agave nectar**

1 **tablespoon grated peeled fresh ginger or refrigerated ginger paste**

Ice cubes

1 Pour coconut water into large pitcher. Add cucumber, lime juice, agave, and ginger, stirring until mixed well.

2 Refrigerate at least 2 hours or up to 1 day. Pour into 4 ice-filled glasses.

3 **SmartPoints value per serving** (1 cup without ice): 63 Cal, 5 g Total Fat, 4 g Sat Fat, 66 mg Sod, 4 g Total Carb, 2 g Sugar, 1 g Fib, 0 g Prot.

Lotsa fruit spritzers

Serves 6

 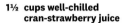

1½ cups well-chilled
cran-strawberry juice

1½ cups well-chilled
guava–passion fruit juice
or tropical fruit medley

Juice of 1 large lime

3 cups well-chilled
plain seltzer

Ice cubes

Lime wedges and whole
strawberries

Stir together cran-strawberry juice, guava–passion fruit juice, and lime juice in pitcher. Add seltzer and pour into 6 ice-filled glasses. Garnish with lime wedges and strawberries.

 SmartPoints value per serving (1 cup without ice): 66 Cal, 0 g Total Fat, 0 g Sat Fat, 45 mg Sod, 17 g Total Carb, 14 g Sugar, 1 g Fib, 1 g Prot.

Mustardy deviled eggs

Serves 6

Who doesn't love a good deviled egg? Our recipe rivals any version you've had of this American classic. A small amount of piquant Dijon mustard mixed with just a touch of white vinegar is what makes this rendition special.

6	**large eggs**
3	**tablespoons reduced-fat mayonnaise**
1½	**teaspoons Dijon mustard**
1	**teaspoon white vinegar**
¼	**teaspoon hot pepper sauce**
¼	**teaspoon black pepper plus additional for sprinkling**
⅛	**teaspoon salt**

1 Put eggs in medium saucepan and add enough cold water to cover by at least 1 inch; bring to boil. Immediately remove saucepan from heat. Let stand, covered, 12 minutes. Pour off water and rinse eggs under cold running water to cool slightly.

2 Peel eggs and cut lengthwise in half. Remove yolks and transfer to small bowl; mash with fork until smooth. Add all remaining ingredients and stir until combined well.

3 Spoon yolk mixture into small plastic bag and snip off one corner or spoon into pastry bag fitted with star tip. Pipe evenly into egg-white halves. Arrange deviled eggs on platter and sprinkle with black pepper. Serve or cover loosely and refrigerate up to 4 hours. Let stand 15 minutes at room temperature before serving for best flavor.

1 **SmartPoints value per serving** (2 deviled egg halves): 98 Cal, 7 g Total Fat, 2 g Sat Fat, 207 mg Sod, 1 g Total Carb, 1 g Sugar, 0 g Fib, 6 g Prot.

Chunky guacamole-topped rice cakes

Serves 4

If you're someone who likes finely diced red onion and/or chopped fresh cilantro in your guacamole, don't hesitate to add them to our tasty guac for 0 SmartPoints.

1	**Hass avocado, halved, pitted, and peeled**
1	**plum tomato, chopped**
½	**jalapeño pepper, seeded and minced**
2	**teaspoons lime juice**
¼	**teaspoon salt**
4	**(4-inch) thin square rice cakes, such as brown rice or rice-quinoa blend**

Coarsely mash avocado in medium bowl. Add tomato, jalapeño, lime juice, and salt, gently stirring to combine. Top rice cakes evenly with guacamole and arrange on platter.

 SmartPoints value per serving (1 guacamole-topped rice cake): 123 Cal, 8 g Total Fat, 1 g Sat Fat, 152 mg Sod, 13 g Total Carb, 1 g Sugar, 4 g Fib, 2 g Prot.

Chunky guacamole-topped rice cakes

Crab salad-topped cucumber

Serves 4

The crab salad—simple and elegant—is delectable as is. But when a bit of flavor oomph is called for, add a generous squeeze of fresh lime or lemon juice as well as a pinch of cayenne or a few shakes of your favorite hot sauce.

¼ **pound lump crabmeat, picked over and flaked**

2 **tablespoons mayonnaise**

2 **tablespoons finely chopped fresh chives**

1 **tablespoon finely chopped celery**

¼ **teaspoon salt**

⅛ **teaspoon black pepper**

20 **(¼-inch) slices English (seedless) cucumber**

1 Gently stir together crabmeat, mayonnaise, chives, celery, salt, and pepper in small bowl.

2 Spoon about 1 teaspoon crab mixture onto each cucumber slice. Arrange on platter and serve, or loosely cover and refrigerate up to 2 hours.

2 **SmartPoints value per serving** (5 crab-topped cucumber slices): 78 Cal, 6 g Total Fat, 1 g Sat Fat, 276 mg Sod, 1 g Total Carb, 1 g Sugar, 0 g Fib, 6 g Prot.

Greek tzatziki dip

Serves 6

Who doesn't love tzatziki, the beloved Greek cucumber-yogurt dip? Nothing could be easier than a recipe where all that is required is stirring ingredients together in a bowl.

½ **English (seedless) cucumber, cut into ¼-inch dice**

1 **cup plain reduced-fat Greek yogurt**

2 **tablespoons chopped fresh dill**

1 **teaspoon ground cumin**

¼ **teaspoon salt**

⅛–¼ **teaspoon black pepper**

Stir together all ingredients in serving bowl. Serve or cover and refrigerate up to 4 days.

 SmartPoints value per serving (scant ⅓ cup): 32 Cal, 1 g Total Fat, 1 g Sat Fat, 112 mg Sod, 3 g Total Carb, 1 g Sugar, 0 g Fib, 4 g Prot.

Freestyle it

If you haven't tried adding diced ripe mango to tzatziki, this is your opportunity. It adds a welcome bit of fruitiness that makes this dip even better—and for 0 SmartPoints.

Provençal tomato tart

Serves 12

In this tasty pick-up-and-eat appetizer, a light and crisp phyllo-dough shell surrounds juicy slices of ripe tomato. Scattered on top are temptingly salty Kalamata olives and grated Parmesan cheese, while ever so thinly sliced onion adds the right touch.

5	large red or yellow plum tomatoes or a combination, cut into ¼-inch slices
1	onion, very thinly sliced
16	pitted Kalamata olives, quartered
½	teaspoon salt
¼	teaspoon black pepper
8	(12 x 17-inch) sheets phyllo dough, thawed if frozen
½	cup grated Parmesan cheese

1 Set oven rack in lower third of oven and preheat oven to 425°F.

2 Meanwhile, place tomato slices between double thickness of paper towels and pat dry. Let stand 10 minutes.

3 Toss together onion, olives, salt, and pepper in small bowl.

4 Lay 1 phyllo sheet on large baking sheet and lightly spray with olive oil nonstick spray. (Keep remaining phyllo covered with damp kitchen towel and plastic wrap to prevent it from drying out.) Repeat layering with remaining 7 sheets of phyllo, spraying each sheet with nonstick spray. Roll edges of phyllo in to form rim.

5 Arrange tomato slices on phyllo in single overlapping layer. Top with onion mixture and lightly spray with nonstick spray. Bake until bottom and edges of phyllo are golden and tomatoes and onion are softened, 25–35 minutes. Sprinkle with Parmesan. Cut tart into 12 equal pieces. Serve hot, warm, or at room temperature.

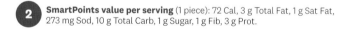

2   **SmartPoints value per serving** (1 piece): 72 Cal, 3 g Total Fat, 1 g Sat Fat, 273 mg Sod, 10 g Total Carb, 1 g Sugar, 1 g Fib, 3 g Prot.

**Provençal
tomato tart**

Edamame-tomato bruschetta

Serves 6

¾	**pound tomatoes, cut into small dice**
¾	**teaspoon salt**
½	**teaspoon black pepper**
1½	**cups frozen shelled edamame**
2	**tablespoons extra-virgin olive oil**
12	**(½-inch) slices whole wheat or whole-grain Italian bread, toasted**
1	**lemon, cut into 6 wedges**

1 Stir together tomatoes, ¼ teaspoon of salt, and ¼ teaspoon of pepper in large bowl. Let stand until tomato juices are released, about 20 minutes. Drain tomatoes in sieve set over small bowl; reserve juice.

2 Cook edamame according to package directions. Drain and let cool.

3 Combine edamame, ⅓ cup reserved tomato juice, 1 tablespoon of oil, remaining ½ teaspoon salt, and remaining ¼ teaspoon pepper in food processor and process until it forms a coarse puree, adding a little tomato juice or water if mixture seems dry.

4 Spread 1 rounded tablespoon edamame puree on each toast and top evenly with tomatoes. Drizzle remaining 1 tablespoon oil over tomatoes and serve with lemon wedges.

6 **SmartPoints value per serving** (2 bruschetta): 273 Cal, 9 g Total Fat, 1 g Sat Fat, 588 mg Sod, 35 g Total Carb, 6 g Sugar, 6 g Fib, 13 g Prot.

Add this
Sprinkle each bruschetta with thinly sliced fresh mint or basil for a touch of bright flavor.

Reuben-style quesadillas

Serves 8

A Reuben is a classic deli sandwich of corned beef, coleslaw, Swiss cheese, Thousand Island dressing, and sauerkraut layered between slices of fresh bread. We've slimmed it down by substituting roast turkey for the corned beef.

½ **cup Thousand Island dressing**

4 **(7-inch) reduced-fat whole wheat tortillas**

1 **(¼-pound) piece skinless roasted turkey, shredded**

1 **cup tightly packed coleslaw mix**

½ **cup shredded reduced-fat Swiss cheese**

1 Spread 1 tablespoon of dressing on one half of each tortilla. Layer one-fourth of turkey, coleslaw, and Swiss cheese over dressing. Fold unfilled half of each tortilla over filling, gently pressing down. Spray tops of quesadillas with nonstick spray.

2 Place 2 quesadillas, sprayed-side down, in large skillet and set over medium-high heat. Cook until crisp and browned in spots, about 3 minutes. Spray tops of quesadillas with nonstick spray and turn over. Cook until browned in spots and cheese is melted, about 2 minutes longer.

3 Transfer quesadillas to cutting board and cover to keep warm. Repeat with remaining 2 quesadillas. Cut each quesadilla in half. Serve with remaining ¼ cup dressing.

4 **SmartPoints value per serving** (½ quesadilla and 1½ teaspoons dressing): 154 Cal, 7 g Total Fat, 1 g Sat Fat, 314 mg Sod, 15 g Total Carb, 4 g Sugar, 1 g Fib, 8 g Prot.

Freestyle it

We left the sauerkraut out of our Reuben quesadillas. If you like, however, spread a thin layer of well-drained 0 SmartPoints canned or bagged sauerkraut over the slaw.

**Parmesan-pepper
green bean "fries"**

Parmesan-pepper green bean "fries"

Serves 6

2	large egg whites, at room temperature
2	tablespoons water
1	cup grated Parmesan cheese
1	teaspoon black pepper
¾	pound green beans, trimmed

1 Preheat oven to 425°F. Line large rimmed baking sheet with silicone baking mat or sheet of parchment paper.

2 Whisk together egg whites and water in shallow bowl until foamy. In another shallow bowl, mix together Parmesan and pepper.

3 Dip green beans, one at a time, into egg-white mixture allowing excess to drip off. Coat beans with Parmesan and arrange on prepared baking sheet about 1 inch apart.

4 Bake until Parmesan is melted and lightly browned, about 8 minutes. Transfer green beans with baking sheet to wire rack and let cool slightly before serving.

2 **SmartPoints value per serving** (⅙ of green beans): 94 Cal, 5 g Total Fat, 3 g Sat Fat, 323 mg Sod, 7 g Total Carb, 1 g Sugar, 2 g Fib, 7 g Prot.

Root vegetable chips

Serves 8

Crisp vegetable chips have taken off as a smarter-than-potato-chips snack choice—and for good reason. They have better stats and are über flavorful. Ours are no exception.

1   **very large carrot, peeled**

1   **very large parsnip, peeled**

1   **small sweet potato, scrubbed**

¾   **teaspoon kosher salt**

Pinch cayenne

1 Preheat oven to 400°F. Line two large rimmed baking sheets with nonstick foil.

2 Cut carrot, parsnip, and sweet potato into ⅛-inch slices using vegetable slicer or thin slicing blade of food processor. Combine vegetables in large bowl and generously spray with olive oil nonstick spray, tossing to coat evenly. Sprinkle vegetables with salt and cayenne, tossing to coat.

3 Arrange vegetables in single layer on prepared baking sheets. Bake until lightly browned, about 30 minutes, rotating baking sheets halfway through baking time and transferring vegetables to large bowl as they are browned. (Chips will crisp a bit as they cool.)

1   **SmartPoints value per serving** (about ½ cup): 41 Cal, 0 g Total Fat, 0 g Sat Fat, 199 mg Sod, 10 g Total Carb, 3 g Sugar, 2 g Fib, 1 g Prot.

Cheesy kale crisps

Serves 8

Kale chips, also known as crisps, have become all the rage. Making them at home is easy and much less expensive than buying them. Store the chips in an airtight container up to several days.

2	**bunches curly kale, tough stems removed and discarded and leaves torn into 2-inch pieces**
4	**teaspoons canola oil**
1	**teaspoon garlic powder**
½	**teaspoon onion powder**
½	**teaspoon kosher salt**
3	**tablespoons grated pecorino-Romano cheese**

1 Preheat oven to 350°F. Spray two large baking sheets with nonstick spray.

2 Put kale in very large bowl. Drizzle with oil and toss until evenly coated. Sprinkle with garlic powder, onion powder, and salt and toss until mixed well.

3 Spread kale on prepared baking sheets to form single layer. Bake until crisp, about 20 minutes. Let cool slightly; sprinkle with Romano.

1 **SmartPoints value per serving** (about 1¼ cups): 74 Cal, 4 g Total Fat, 1 g Sat Fat, 187 mg Sod, 8 g Total Carb, 2 g Sugar, 3 g Fib, 4 g Prot.

Lemon and
pecorino
popcorn

Lemon and pecorino popcorn

Serves 8

It might surprise you to know that the oldest popped kernels of corn were discovered in a cave in New Mexico back in 1948. The popped corn was then carbon dated and shown to be about 5,600 years old!

8   **cups plain air-popped popcorn**
1   **tablespoon olive oil**
1   **tablespoon chopped fresh thyme**
1   **teaspoon grated lemon zest**
½   **teaspoon salt**
6   **tablespoons grated pecorino-Romano cheese**

Put popcorn into very large bowl. Drizzle with oil, thyme, lemon zest, and salt, tossing to coat popcorn evenly. Gradually sprinkle Romano over popcorn, tossing to coat evenly.

2 **SmartPoints value per serving** (1 cup): 61 Cal, 3 g Total Fat, 1 g Sat Fat, 222 mg Sod, 6 g Total Carb, 0 g Sugar, 1 g Fib, 2 g Prot.

Chapter 3
Big and small soups and salads

Silky chickpea soup with cumin

Serves 6

Chickpea (garbanzo) flour is made from ground dried chickpeas. It can be found in most supermarkets—look for Bob's Red Mill—and in specialty food stores. It's used to make socca, crêpes that are sold on the streets of Provence.

1 tablespoon cumin seeds

5½ cups water

2 large garlic cloves, minced

1¼ teaspoons salt

1 cup chickpea flour

2 tablespoons lemon juice plus 6 very thin lemon wedges

1 tablespoon fruity extra-virgin olive oil

1 Put cumin seeds in medium saucepan and toast over medium heat, shaking pan occasionally, until seeds deepen slightly in color and are fragrant, about 2 minutes. Transfer ½ teaspoon of toasted seeds to cup and reserve.

2 Add 4½ cups of water, the garlic, and salt to same saucepan and bring to boil. Reduce heat and simmer until flavors are blended, about 5 minutes.

3 Meanwhile, whisk together chickpea flour and remaining 1 cup water in medium bowl or glass measure until smooth, then gradually whisk into water-garlic mixture in saucepan. Cook, whisking occasionally, until soup has thickened, about 3 minutes.

4 Remove saucepan from heat and stir in lemon juice. Ladle soup evenly into 6 bowls and sprinkle with reserved cumin seeds. Drizzle each serving with ½ teaspoon oil and top with lemon slice.

3 **SmartPoints value per serving** (1 cup): 88 Cal, 4 g Total Fat, 0 g Sat Fat, 503 mg Sod, 11 g Total Carb, 2 g Sugar, 2 g Fib, 4 g Prot.

**Silky chickpea soup
with cumin**

Fresh corn-basil soup

Serves 6

1	**tablespoon canola oil**
1	**onion, chopped**
3	**large garlic cloves, minced**
3	**cups corn kernels (about 6 ears of corn)**
1	**(32-ounce) carton vegetable broth**
½	**teaspoon salt**
¼	**teaspoon black pepper**
	Thinly sliced fresh basil leaves

1 Heat oil in large pot or Dutch oven over medium heat. Add onion and cook, stirring, until softened, about 5 minutes. Add garlic and cook, stirring, until fragrant, about 30 seconds. Add corn and cook, stirring, until tender, about 5 minutes. Stir in broth, salt, and pepper and bring to boil. Reduce heat and simmer 10 minutes. Remove pot from heat and let cool 10 minutes.

2 Transfer 3 cups of soup to blender and blend until smooth. Return to pot and cook over low heat until heated through, about 2 minutes. Ladle soup evenly into 6 bowls and sprinkle with basil.

1 **SmartPoints value per serving** (1 cup): 137 Cal, 4 g Total Fat, 0 g Sat Fat, 649 mg Sod, 26 g Total Carb, 6 g Sugar, 3 g Fib, 4 g Prot.

Miso soup with tofu and scallions

Serves 4

Lunch or dinner in a Japanese restaurant invariably begins with a choice of a green salad topped with carrot-ginger dressing or a bowl of delicately flavored miso soup studded with bits of scallion. Our flavorful rendition rivals any you've had.

4	**cups water**
1	**(14-ounce) package firm tofu, diced**
½	**pound shiitake mushrooms, stems removed and caps thinly sliced**
6	**scallions, sliced (white and green parts separated)**
½	**teaspoon grated peeled fresh ginger or refrigerated ginger paste**
¼	**cup white miso**
¼	**teaspoon black pepper**

1 Bring water to boil in medium saucepan. Add tofu, mushrooms, white part of scallions, and ¼ teaspoon of ginger and bring to boil. Reduce heat and simmer until flavors are blended, about 5 minutes.

2 Ladle about ½ cup of liquid into small bowl and whisk in miso until smooth. Stir miso mixture back into saucepan and remove from heat.

3 Stir green part of scallions, remaining ¼ teaspoon ginger, and pepper into soup. Ladle soup evenly into 4 bowls.

1 **SmartPoints value per serving** (1¼ cups): 137 Cal, 5 g Total Fat, 1 g Sat Fat, 652 mg Sod, 13 g Total Carb, 2 g Sugar, 4 g Fib, 13 g Prot.

North African red lentil soup

Serves 4

Simple yet exotic is the best way to describe this boldly flavored soup. The marriage of tomatoes with red lentils, ground cumin, cilantro, and yogurt will transport you to far-flung places where you've always dreamed of traveling.

3	**cups water**
1	**(14½-ounce) can diced tomatoes with garlic and onions**
1	**cup dried red lentils, picked over and rinsed**
1	**teaspoon ground cumin**
¾	**teaspoon salt**
¼	**teaspoon black pepper**
⅓	**cup chopped fresh cilantro**
½	**cup plain low-fat yogurt**

1 Combine water, tomatoes, lentils, cumin, salt, and pepper in medium saucepan and bring to boil. Reduce heat and simmer, covered, stirring occasionally, until lentils are tender, about 30 minutes.

2 Remove saucepan from heat and stir in cilantro. Ladle soup evenly into 4 bowls. Top each serving with 2-tablespoon dollop of yogurt. If reheating, thin soup with water if needed.

 SmartPoints value per serving (1 cup soup and 2 tablespoons yogurt): 218 Cal, 1 g Total Fat, 0 g Sat Fat, 861 mg Sod, 38 g Total Carb, 7 g Sugar, 6 g Fib, 14 g Prot.

**North African
red lentil soup**

Soba noodle–
mushroom soup

Soba noodle-mushroom soup

Serves 6

3   ounces soba (100% buckwheat) noodles

6   cups chicken broth

1   tablespoon white miso

¼   pound shiitake mushrooms, stems removed and caps sliced

4   cups lightly packed baby spinach

1 Cook noodles according to package directions. Drain in colander and rinse under cool running water; drain again.

2 Meanwhile, whisk together broth and miso in large saucepan. Add mushrooms and bring to boil. Reduce heat and simmer until mushrooms are tender, about 5 minutes. Stir in noodles and spinach and cook until noodles are heated through and spinach has wilted, about 3 minutes longer.

2 **SmartPoints value per serving** (about 1 cup): 105 Cal, 2 g Total Fat, 0 g Sat Fat, 883 mg Sod, 14 g Total Carb, 2 g Sugar, 2 g Fib, 8 g Prot.

Freestyle it

To make this soup heartier and for 0 SmartPoints, add ¼ pound cooked small shrimp (pictured) or picked over lump crabmeat along with the noodles in step 2. Dress up each serving by sprinkling with chopped fresh chives, if you like.

**Pea soup with
smoked salmon**

Pea soup with smoked salmon

Serves 6

Smoked salmon and chives are a wonderful match. Sprinkle each serving of soup with finely chopped fresh chives for a bit of delicate onion flavor.

2	**(14½-ounce) cans chicken broth**
1	**large baking potato, peeled and diced**
1	**onion, chopped**
1	**(16-ounce) bag frozen baby peas**
¼	**teaspoon salt**
¼	**plus ⅛ teaspoon black pepper**
2	**ounces thinly sliced smoked salmon, diced or cut crosswise into thin strips**

1 Combine broth, potato, and onion in large saucepan and bring to boil. Reduce heat and simmer until potato is fork-tender, about 10 minutes. Stir in peas, salt, and ¼ teaspoon of pepper and cook until peas are tender, about 5 minutes.

2 Remove saucepan from heat and let cool 10 minutes. Pour soup into blender, in batches if needed, and blend until smooth. Return soup to saucepan and cook over low heat until heated through, about 2 minutes. Ladle soup evenly into 6 bowls, top with salmon, and sprinkle with remaining ⅛ teaspoon pepper.

 SmartPoints value per serving (1 cup soup and 1½ tablespoons smoked salmon): 145 Cal, 2 g Total Fat, 0 g Sat Fat, 788 mg Sod, 23 g Total Carb, 6 g Sugar, 5 g Fib, 10 g Prot.

Simple potato-leek soup

Serves 6

To clean leeks, trim the roots leaving the root ends intact. Cut the leeks lengthwise in half and fan open the layers. Swish the leeks in a large bowl of cool water to release any grit. Lift out the leeks and slice or chop as directed.

1¾ **pounds Yukon Gold potatoes, peeled and cut into ¾-inch chunks**

4 **large leeks (white and pale green parts only), thinly sliced**

1 **large onion, chopped**

5 **cups chicken broth**

½ **teaspoon salt**

¼ **teaspoon black pepper**

Chopped fresh chives

1 Combine potatoes, leeks, onion, broth, salt, and pepper in large pot or Dutch oven and bring to boil. Reduce heat and simmer, covered, until vegetables are tender, about 25 minutes. Remove pot from heat and let cool 10 minutes.

2 Pour soup into blender, in batches if needed, and blend until smooth. Return soup to pot and cook over low heat until heated through, about 2 minutes. Taste and season with salt and pepper, if needed. Ladle soup evenly into 6 bowls and sprinkle with chives.

3 **SmartPoints value per serving** (1⅓ cups): 175 Cal, 2 g Total Fat, 0 g Sat Fat, 849 mg Sod, 33 g Total Carb, 6 g Sugar, 5 g Fib, 8 g Prot.

Thai egg drop soup

Serves 4

We love this simple egg drop soup just the way it is, but for 0 SmartPoints you can stir in a handful or two of tender watercress sprigs and 1 cup of diced firm tofu.

1 **(32-ounce) carton chicken broth**

1 **teaspoon Thai green curry paste or to taste**

3 **large eggs, lightly beaten**

1 **small scallion, thinly sliced**

2 **tablespoons chopped fresh cilantro**

¼ **teaspoon salt or to taste**

1 Whisk together broth and curry paste in large saucepan and bring to boil. Reduce heat and simmer 8 minutes.

2 Gradually add eggs in slow, steady stream, gently stirring constantly to form threads of egg. Cook, stirring constantly, 1 minute. Remove saucepan from heat and stir in scallion, cilantro, and salt. Ladle evenly into 4 bowls.

1 **SmartPoints value per serving** (1 cup): 94 Cal, 5 g Total Fat, 2 g Sat Fat, 906 mg Sod, 2 g Total Carb, 1 g Sugar, 0 g Fib, 9 g Prot.

Coconut-curry tomato soup

Serves 4

This zesty soup will transport you to exotic places you've dreamed of traveling to. Cooking the curry paste in oil releases all its complexity. Coconut milk then rounds out the flavors, while tomatoes and lime juice add just the right note of acidity.

2	**teaspoons canola oil**
1¼	**teaspoons Thai red curry paste or to taste**
2	**(14½-ounce) cans petite diced tomatoes**
1	**(13.66-ounce) can light (low-fat) coconut milk**
¼	**teaspoon salt**
2	**teaspoons lime juice**
⅓	**cup lightly packed fresh cilantro leaves, coarsely chopped**

1 Heat oil in large saucepan over medium heat. Add curry paste and cook, stirring constantly, until fragrant, about 1 minute. Stir in tomatoes, coconut milk, and salt and bring to boil. Reduce heat and simmer, covered, 3 minutes.

2 Remove saucepan from heat and stir in lime juice. Ladle soup evenly into 4 bowls and sprinkle with cilantro.

5 **SmartPoints value per serving** (1¼ cups): 130 Cal, 9 g Total Fat, 6 g Sat Fat, 462 mg Sod, 12 g Total Carb, 5 g Sugar, 2 g Fib, 2 g Prot.

Chickpea-broccoli soup

Serves 4

For a delicious variation on this fast and tasty soup, use cauliflower instead of the broccoli and cannellini (white kidney) beans instead of the chickpeas.

2	teaspoons olive oil
1	large garlic clove, minced
2	cups water
1	cup canned crushed tomatoes
¼	teaspoon salt or to taste
¼	teaspoon black pepper or to taste
2	cups small broccoli florets
1	cup canned chickpeas, rinsed and drained
¼	cup grated Parmesan cheese

1 Heat oil in medium saucepan over medium heat. Add garlic and cook, stirring constantly, until fragrant, about 30 seconds.

2 Add water, tomatoes, salt, and pepper and bring to boil. Add broccoli and chickpeas; reduce heat and simmer, covered, stirring occasionally, until broccoli is tender, about 5 minutes.

3 Ladle soup evenly into 4 bowls and sprinkle with Parmesan.

 SmartPoints value per serving (about 1 cup soup and 1 tablespoon Parmesan): 156 Cal, 6 g Total Fat, 1 g Sat Fat, 513 mg Sod, 20 g Total Carb, 5 g Sugar, 5 g Fib, 8 g Prot.

Freestyle it
Before adding the garlic to the saucepan, cook 1 small onion, chopped, in the oil until softened, about 5 minutes, for another tasty layer of flavor for 0 SmartPoints.

Roast beef and Napa cabbage slaw

Serves 4

½ cup gluten-free reduced-fat sesame-ginger dressing

2 teaspoons grated peeled fresh ginger

6 cups lightly packed thinly sliced Napa cabbage

2 cups matchstick-cut carrots

6 (1-ounce) slices lean roast beef, trimmed and cut into strips

Black pepper

Whisk together 6 tablespoons of dressing and the ginger in large bowl. Add cabbage and carrots and toss until coated evenly. Divide evenly among 4 plates and top evenly with roast beef. Sprinkle salads with pepper and drizzle with remaining 2 tablespoons dressing.

 SmartPoints value per serving (about 2 cups slaw and 1½ slices roast beef): 196 Cal, 6 g Total Fat, 1 g Sat Fat, 410 mg Sod, 23 g Total Carb, 14 g Sugar, 5 g Fib, 14 g Prot.

Greens with Gorgonzola and almonds

Serves 4

5 tablespoons reduced-fat raspberry vinaigrette

1 shallot, thinly sliced

1 (7-ounce) container mixed baby salad greens

¼ cup crumbled Gorgonzola or goat cheese

2 tablespoons chopped smoked almonds

Combine vinaigrette and shallot in large bowl. Add salad greens and toss until coated evenly. Add Gorgonzola and toss until combined. Divide salad evenly among 4 plates and sprinkle with almonds.

 SmartPoints value per serving (1½ cups salad and ½ tablespoon almonds): 129 Cal, 10 g Total Fat, 3 g Sat Fat, 509 mg Sod, 5 g Total Carb, 2 g Sugar, 2 g Fib, 6 g Prot.

Niçoise-inspired tuna salad

Niçoise-inspired tuna salad

Serves 4

Niçoise salad originated in the city of Nice in France. Serve our version on a bed of Bibb lettuce leaves.

Grated zest and juice of 1 large lemon

2   **cups packaged fully cooked diced potatoes, at room temperature**

1   **large tomato, diced**

16   **niçoise olives, pitted if desired**

½   **teaspoon salt**

¼   **teaspoon black pepper**

1   **(5-ounce) can water-packed light tuna, drained and flaked**

Combine lemon zest and juice in serving bowl. Add potatoes, tomato, olives, salt, and pepper and toss until mixed well. Gently stir in tuna.

3 **SmartPoints value per serving** (about 1 cup): 138 Cal, 2 g Total Fat, 0 g Sat Fat, 514 mg Sod, 22 g Total Carb, 2 g Sugar, 4 g Fib, 11 g Prot.

Warm roasted butternut squash salad

Serves 4

1	(20-ounce) package peeled and seeded butternut squash chunks
½	teaspoon salt
¼	teaspoon black pepper
1	(5-ounce) container baby kale, baby arugula, mizuna, and radicchio salad mix
⅓	cup reduced-fat red-wine vinaigrette
¼	cup coarsely chopped walnuts, toasted
¼	cup crumbled soft goat cheese

1 Preheat oven to 425°F. Spray rimmed baking sheet with olive oil nonstick spray.

2 Put squash on prepared baking sheet. Spray with nonstick spray and sprinkle with salt and pepper; toss until evenly coated and spread to form even layer.

3 Roast squash, turning halfway through roasting time, until tender and lightly browned, about 25 minutes. Let cool slightly.

4 Put salad mix in large bowl. Drizzle with vinaigrette and toss until coated evenly. Divide salad evenly among 4 plates. Top evenly with squash and sprinkle with walnuts and goat cheese.

 SmartPoints value per serving (2 cups greens, ¾ cup squash, 1 tablespoon walnuts, and 1 tablespoon goat cheese): 187 Cal, 10 g Total Fat, 3 g Sat Fat, 587 mg Sod, 21 g Total Carb, 5 g Sugar, 4 g Fib, 6 g Prot.

Warm roasted butternut squash salad

Romaine and sun-dried tomato salad

Serves 4

Our red, white, and green salad mimics the colors of the boldly striped Italian flag. Save a bit of prep time by using moist-packed sun-dried tomatoes, which don't need to be soaked in hot water. You can find them in Italian markets and specialty food stores.

16	sun-dried tomato halves (not oil-packed)
4	cups lightly packed thinly sliced romaine lettuce
4	ounces part-skim mozzarella cheese, diced
¼	teaspoon salt
¼	teaspoon black pepper
2	tablespoons good-quality balsamic vinegar

1 Combine sun-dried tomatoes with enough hot water to cover in small bowl and let stand until tomatoes have softened, about 10 minutes. Drain, pat dry with paper towels, and chop.

2 Meanwhile, combine romaine, mozzarella, salt, and pepper in salad bowl. Add sun-dried tomatoes and vinegar and toss until coated evenly.

3 **SmartPoints value per serving** (about 1⅓ cups): 108 Cal, 5 g Total Fat, 3 g Sat Fat, 335 mg Sod, 8 g Total Carb, 5 g Sugar, 2 g Fib, 9 g Prot.

Freestyle it

For a welcome bit of crunch and no additional Smartpoints, sprinkle each serving of salad with ½ tablespoon of pumpkin (pepita) seeds.

South-of-the-border salad

Serves 6

1   poblano chile
4   cups lightly packed
    chopped romaine lettuce
2   cups matchstick-cut jicama
    (about ½ pound)
16 grape tomatoes, halved
½   cup black bean–corn salsa

1 Preheat broiler. Line small heavy rimmed baking sheet with foil.

2 Place poblano on prepared baking sheet and broil 5 inches from heat, turning occasionally, until charred, about 5 minutes. Transfer chile to small zip-close plastic bag; seal and let steam about 10 minutes.

3 When cool enough to handle, remove charred peel and seeds from chile and discard. Coarsely chop chile and combine with romaine, jicama, tomatoes, and salsa in salad bowl. Toss until mixed well.

0   **SmartPoints value per serving** (about 1 cup): 48 Cal, 1 g Total Fat, 0 g Sat Fat, 51 mg Sod, 11 g Total Carb, 3 g Sugar, 4 g Fib, 2 g Prot.

Chunky cucumber-yogurt salad

Serves 4

Because cucumbers tend to weep if they sit too long after being sliced, this salad is best eaten the day it's prepared.

¾   **cup plain low-fat yogurt**

2   **teaspoons white vinegar**

¼   **cup chopped fresh dill**

½   **teaspoon salt**

¼   **teaspoon black pepper**

4   **cucumbers, peeled, halved lengthwise, seeded, and cut into ¼-inch slices**

1   **small red onion, very thinly sliced**

1 To make dressing, whisk together yogurt, vinegar, dill, salt, and pepper in small bowl.

2 Combine cucumbers and onion in serving bowl. Add dressing and toss until coated evenly.

 SmartPoints value per serving (1¼ cups): 64 Cal, 1 g Total Fat, 1 g Sat Fat, 328 mg Sod, 11 g Total Carb, 7 g Sugar, 2 g Fib, 4 g Prot.

Add this
Toss some chopped fresh mint into the salad along with the yogurt and dill in step 1.

Chunky cucumber-yogurt salad

Fresh pea salad with bacon

Serves 4

Mint and peas are a classic combo. If you happen to have fresh mint on hand—or growing in your garden—scatter thinly sliced or torn leaves over each serving.

1	**cup fresh or thawed frozen peas**
6	**slices packaged fully cooked bacon**
4	**ounces pea shoots or sprouts**
2	**scallions, sliced**
⅓	**cup reduced-fat olive oil vinaigrette**

1 Bring small saucepan of water to boil. Add peas and cook until tender, about 3 minutes. Drain in colander and rinse under cold running water; drain again.

2 Heat bacon in microwave according to package directions. Crumble and set aside.

3 Combine peas, pea shoots, and scallions in large bowl. Drizzle with vinaigrette and toss until coated evenly. Divide salad evenly among 4 plates and top with bacon.

3 **SmartPoints value per serving** (about 1½ cups salad and 1½ slices bacon): 125 Cal, 7 g Total Fat, 2 g Sat Fat, 550 mg Sod, 8 g Total Carb, 4 g Sugar, 3 g Fib, 7 g Prot.

Double orange-mint salad

Serves 6

This unusual salad, a great starter or side dish for simply grilled chicken breast or fish, gets its distinctive flavor from orange flower water, which is distilled from orange blossoms and is used in Mediterranean cuisines.

3   blood oranges, peeled, sliced into rounds, and seeded

3   navel oranges, peeled, sliced into rounds, and seeded

¼–½ teaspoon orange flower water

Pinch–⅛ teaspoon finely ground black pepper

2   tablespoons confectioners' sugar

24 mint leaves, torn if large

1 Combine oranges in large bowl and sprinkle with orange flower water; gently toss. Arrange oranges on platter in decorative pattern; sprinkle with pepper. Cover oranges with plastic wrap and refrigerate up to 1 hour.

2 To serve, dust oranges with confectioners' sugar and scatter mint leaves on top.

① **SmartPoints value per serving** (1 orange): 85 Cal, 0 g Total Fat, 0 g Sat Fat, 0 mg Sod, 21 g Total Carb, 17 g Sugar, 4 g Fib, 2 g Prot.

Add this

Mix the confectioners' sugar with ¼ teaspoon ground cinnamon for an additional layer of flavor.

Red quinoa salad with oranges

Serves 4

A tangle of tempting textures and flavors best describes this unusual salad. Whole-grain, gluten-free quinoa is the perfect foil for the slightly bitter radishes, juicy navel oranges, and salty feta. If you've not had radish tops, this is your chance—you'll love 'em.

1	**cup red quinoa, rinsed**
3	**navel oranges**
4	**large radishes with tops, radishes halved and thinly sliced and tops torn**
¼	**cup reduced-fat red-wine vinaigrette**
½	**teaspoon salt**
¼	**teaspoon black pepper**
¼	**cup plus 2 tablespoons crumbled reduced-fat feta cheese**

1 Prepare quinoa according to package directions. Let cool.

2 Meanwhile, halve and squeeze juice from 1 orange (you should have about ⅓ cup). Pour into salad bowl. Cut sections from remaining 2 oranges and add to bowl.

3 Add cooled quinoa, radishes and tops, vinaigrette, salt, and pepper to orange mixture and gently toss until mixed well. Sprinkle with feta.

6 **SmartPoints value per serving** (about 1 cup): 250 Cal, 6 g Total Fat, 1 g Sat Fat, 591 mg Sod, 42 g Total Carb, 10 g Sugar, 6 g Fib, 9 g Prot.

Red quinoa salad
with oranges

Sumac-dusted onion and chickpeas

Serves 6

Ground sumac, made from the dried berries of a sumac bush that grows in the Middle East and in parts of Italy, is a beautiful dark red powder with a somewhat coarse texture and a tart lemony flavor.

1	**small red onion, thinly sliced (about ¾ cup)**
2	**teaspoons ground sumac**
¼	**cup plus 2 teaspoons reduced-fat balsamic vinaigrette**
2	**(15½-ounce) cans chickpeas, rinsed and drained**
½	**cup lightly packed torn fresh mint**
¼	**teaspoon salt or to taste**

1 Put onion in small bowl; sprinkle with sumac and drizzle with 2 teaspoons of vinaigrette. Toss with your hands, gently massaging sumac into onion. Let stand, tossing occasionally, until onion is wilted, about 30 minutes.

2 Stir together chickpeas, mint, remaining ¼ cup vinaigrette, and salt in serving bowl and top with onions.

 SmartPoints value per serving (⅔ cup): 151 Cal, 4 g Total Fat, 0 g Sat Fat, 750 mg Sod, 22 g Total Carb, 1 g Sugar, 7 g Fib, 7 g Prot.

Freestyle it
The addition of fresh fruit would add a bit of fruity zing to this made-for-fall salad. For 0 SmartPoints, add thinly sliced or diced unpeeled red-skinned pear or apple to the salad so it gets coated with the vinaigrette.

Sumac-dusted onion and chickpeas

Chapter 4
Main event

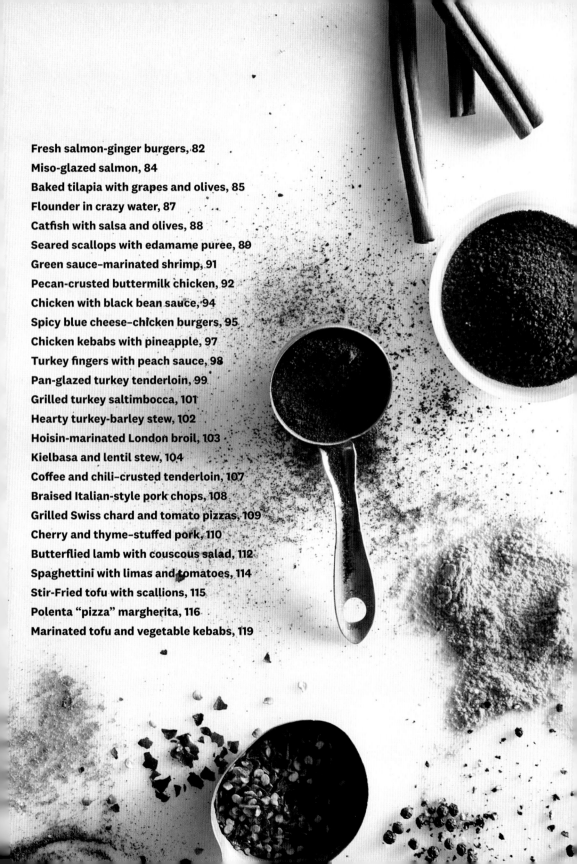

Fresh salmon-ginger burgers

Serves 4

To get the most ginger flavor, shape the patties, place them on a wax paper–lined plate, and cover and refrigerate at least 2 hours or up to 6 hours before cooking so the flavor has time to develop.

1	**slice white or whole wheat sandwich bread**
2	**tablespoons minced peeled fresh ginger**
8	**teaspoons prepared horseradish sauce, such as cranberry-horseradish**
1	**pound skinless salmon fillet, cut into 1-inch pieces**
¼	**teaspoon salt**
¼	**teaspoon black pepper**
2	**teaspoons canola oil**
¼	**cup reduced-fat mayonnaise**

1 Tear bread into pieces and pulse in food processor until coarse crumbs form. Transfer crumbs to large bowl and add ginger and 4 teaspoons of horseradish sauce. Put salmon into food processor and pulse until coarsely chopped. Add to crumb mixture along with salt and pepper.

2 With fork, gently stir salmon mixture until combined well but not overmixed. With damp hands, shape into 4 (4-inch) patties.

3 Heat oil in large nonstick skillet over medium heat until hot. Add salmon patties and cook until golden brown and just opaque in center, about 3 minutes per side.

4 Stir together mayonnaise and remaining 4 teaspoons horseradish sauce in cup. Dollop evenly onto salmon burgers.

 SmartPoints value per serving (1 salmon burger and 1 tablespoon sauce): 277 Cal, 18 g Total Fat, 4 g Sat Fat, 277 mg Sod, 5 g Total Carb, 1 g Sugar, 1 g Fib, 24 g Prot.

Add this
Get even more taste satisfaction by serving the burgers on whole wheat sandwich thins with lettuce, tomato, and red onion for an extra 3 SmartPoints.

**Fresh salmon-
ginger burgers**

Miso-glazed salmon

Serves 4

2   tablespoons white miso

2   tablespoons reduced-
    sodium soy sauce

1½ teaspoons honey

4   (5-ounce) salmon fillets
    with skin

4   baby bok choy, halved
    lengthwise

1 Line small rimmed baking sheet with sheet of nonstick foil.

2 Stir together miso, soy sauce, and honey in cup. Put salmon on prepared baking sheet. Spoon miso mixture over salmon. Marinate in refrigerator at least 15 minutes or up to 2 hours, turning salmon once or twice.

3 Preheat oven to 425°F.

4 Bake salmon, skin-side down, until just opaque in center, about 15 minutes.

5 Meanwhile, place bok choy in steamer basket and set into large skillet over 1 inch of boiling water. Cover and steam until boy choy is tender, about 6 minutes. To serve, slide spatula under salmon flesh to separate from skin. Serve salmon with bok choy.

1 **SmartPoints value per serving** (1 salmon fillet and 1 bok choy): 315 Cal, 8 g Total Fat, 1 g Sat Fat, 1,258 mg Sod, 23 g Total Carb, 14 g Sugar, 9 g Fib, 43 g Prot.

Baked tilapia with grapes and olives

Serves 4

Looking for a different fish to serve? Mild, white-fleshed, meaty tilapia is a great choice. It's always sold skinless and boneless and holds up well to pan-cooking, baking, grilling, and broiling. For the best choice, go to www.seafoodwatch.org.

1½ cups seedless red grapes, halved

½ plus ⅛ teaspoon salt

4 (5-ounce) tilapia fillets

¼ teaspoon black pepper

⅓ cup pitted Kalamata olives, chopped

2 teaspoons olive oil

¼ cup chopped fresh flat-leaf parsley

1 Preheat oven to 400°F. Spray 9 x 13-inch baking dish with nonstick spray.

2 Spread grapes in prepared baking dish and sprinkle with ⅛ teaspoon of salt. Bake 10 minutes.

3 Remove grapes from oven and stir. Sprinkle tilapia with pepper and remaining ½ teaspoon salt. Arrange fillets over grapes in single layer. Scatter olives on top of fish and drizzle with oil. Bake until fish is just opaque in center, about 15 minutes. Sprinkle with parsley.

2 **SmartPoints value per serving** (1 tilapia fillet and about ⅓ cup grapes): 205 Cal, 6 g Total Fat, 1 g Sat Fat, 560 mg Sod, 13 g Total Carb, 10 g Sugar, 1 g Fib, 27 g Prot.

Flounder in
crazy water

Flounder in crazy water

Serves 4

Pesce all'acqua pazza, which means "fish in crazy water," is a way of poaching fish that seems to have originated with Neapolitan fishermen who used sea water to cook their catch.

12	**large fresh flat-leaf parsley sprigs**
2	**cups water**
4	**garlic cloves, thinly sliced**
4	**teaspoons extra-virgin olive oil**
¾	**teaspoon salt**
¾	**teaspoon black pepper**
1½	**pounds mixed baby heirloom tomatoes (2 pints), halved or quartered if large**
4	**(5- to 6-ounce) flounder fillets**

1 Separate leaves and stems of 8 parsley sprigs; coarsely chop leaves. Reserve remaining 4 sprigs. Place parsley stems in large deep skillet with water, garlic, oil, salt, and pepper; bring to boil. Reduce heat to medium-low and simmer, partially covered, until broth is fragrant and garlic is tender, about 15 minutes.

2 Remove parsley stems from skillet and discard. Add tomatoes and chopped parsley to skillet and return to boil. Reduce heat and simmer, uncovered, until tomatoes are slightly softened, about 4 minutes. Fold ends of flounder under to form neat "packages." With pancake spatula, place fish in skillet and cook, covered, until just opaque in center, about 7 minutes.

3 Using two spatulas, carefully transfer fillets to 4 large shallow bowls or deep plates. Spoon tomato mixture over fish and top with reserved 4 parsley sprigs.

② SmartPoints value per serving (1 flounder fillet and generous ½ cup tomato mixture): 203 Cal, 7 g Total Fat, 1 g Sat Fat, 564 mg Sod, 8 g Total Carb, 4 g Sugar, 2 g Fib, 28 g Prot.

Catfish with salsa and olives

Serves 4

Green olives contribute an earthy, almost smoky, salty flavor to dishes. Brighten up a simple tomato sauce by adding a small amount of finely chopped olives for some depth of flavor or add chopped olives to a favorite salad for some interest.

2	tablespoons all-purpose flour
¼	teaspoon salt
¼	teaspoon black pepper
4	(6-ounce) skinless catfish fillets
1	tablespoon olive oil
1⅓	cups fat-free mild salsa
¼	cup pitted green olives, finely chopped
2	tablespoons chopped fresh flat-leaf parsley or cilantro

1 Stir together flour, salt, and pepper on sheet of wax paper. Coat catfish fillets, one at a time, with flour mixture, pressing so it adheres, shaking off any excess.

2 Heat oil in large heavy nonstick skillet over medium-high heat. Add catfish, in batches if needed, and cook until golden, about 6 minutes per side. Add salsa and olives. Reduce heat and simmer, occasionally spooning salsa mixture over fish, until just opaque throughout, about 5 minutes longer. Sprinkle with parsley.

 SmartPoints value per serving (1 catfish fillet and 3 tablespoons salsa mixture): 236 Cal, 9 g Total Fat, 2 g Sat Fat, 649 mg Sod, 9 g Total Carb, 3 g Sugar, 2 g Fib, 29 g Prot.

Add this

Serve this boldly flavored fish dish alongside cooked brown rice for sopping up the tasty sauce (½ cup of brown rice per serving will up the SmartPoints by 4).

Seared scallops with edamame puree

Serves 4

Sea scallops are usually sold wet—packed in a solution that prevents them from drying out. If your market sells dry, day-boat, or diver scallops, these are the ones to reach for, as they contain no additives.

1¾	**cups frozen shelled edamame**
¾	**teaspoon salt**
1	**cup water**
⅓	**cup fat-free half-and-half, warmed**
½	**teaspoon black pepper**
1	**lemon, halved**
16	**large sea scallops (about 1½ pounds), patted dry**
1½	**teaspoons canola oil**

1 Bring small saucepan of water to boil over high heat. Add edamame and ¼ teaspoon of salt and cook until edamame are tender, about 10 minutes. With slotted spoon, remove ¼ cup of edamame and reserve.

2 Transfer remaining 1½ cups edamame with 1 cup water to blender. Add half-and-half, ¼ teaspoon salt, and ¼ teaspoon of pepper and blend until it forms smooth, thick puree, adding a bit more water if needed. Return puree to saucepan and add juice from 1 lemon half, stirring to combine. Keep warm over very low heat.

3 Sprinkle scallops with remaining ¼ teaspoon salt. Heat oil in large heavy nonstick skillet over medium-high heat until very hot. Add 8 scallops and sear until deep golden brown and barely translucent in center, about 2 minutes per side. Transfer scallops to plate and loosely cover with sheet of foil. Cook remaining 8 scallops.

4 Spoon edamame puree evenly onto 4 plates and top each serving with 4 scallops. Sprinkle with reserved edamame and remaining ¼ teaspoon pepper. Cut remaining lemon half into 4 wedges and place alongside scallops.

1 **SmartPoints value per serving** (4 scallops, ½ cup puree, and 1 tablespoon edamame): 249 Cal, 7 g Total Fat, 1 g Sat Fat, 1,120 mg Sod, 17 g Total Carb, 4 g Sugar, 3 g Fib, 29 g Prot.

Green sauce–
marinated shrimp

Green sauce–
marinated shrimp

Seared scallops with edamame puree

Serves 4

Sea scallops are usually sold wet—packed in a solution that prevents them from drying out. If your market sells dry, day-boat, or diver scallops, these are the ones to reach for, as they contain no additives.

1¾ **cups frozen shelled edamame**

¾ **teaspoon salt**

1 **cup water**

⅓ **cup fat-free half-and-half, warmed**

½ **teaspoon black pepper**

1 **lemon, halved**

16 **large sea scallops (about 1½ pounds), patted dry**

1½ **teaspoons canola oil**

1 Bring small saucepan of water to boil over high heat. Add edamame and ¼ teaspoon of salt and cook until edamame are tender, about 10 minutes. With slotted spoon, remove ¼ cup of edamame and reserve.

2 Transfer remaining 1½ cups edamame with 1 cup water to blender. Add half-and-half, ¼ teaspoon salt, and ¼ teaspoon of pepper and blend until it forms smooth, thick puree, adding a bit more water if needed. Return puree to saucepan and add juice from 1 lemon half, stirring to combine. Keep warm over very low heat.

3 Sprinkle scallops with remaining ¼ teaspoon salt. Heat oil in large heavy nonstick skillet over medium-high heat until very hot. Add 8 scallops and sear until deep golden brown and barely translucent in center, about 2 minutes per side. Transfer scallops to plate and loosely cover with sheet of foil. Cook remaining 8 scallops.

4 Spoon edamame puree evenly onto 4 plates and top each serving with 4 scallops. Sprinkle with reserved edamame and remaining ¼ teaspoon pepper. Cut remaining lemon half into 4 wedges and place alongside scallops.

 SmartPoints value per serving (4 scallops, ½ cup puree, and 1 tablespoon edamame): 249 Cal, 7 g Total Fat, 1 g Sat Fat, 1,120 mg Sod, 17 g Total Carb, 4 g Sugar, 3 g Fib, 29 g Prot.

Pecan-crusted
buttermilk chicken

Chicken with black bean sauce

Serves 4

The key to success when it comes to cooking in a wok is allowing the wok to preheat enough so that the chicken starts to sear the minute it hits the pan. Just listen for the sizzle.

4	teaspoons Asian (dark) sesame oil
1	pound skinless boneless chicken breasts, cut on diagonal into strips
½	teaspoon salt
1	tablespoon grated peeled fresh ginger
1	(1-pound) bunch asparagus, trimmed and cut into 2-inch lengths
3	tablespoons water
¼	cup black bean sauce

1 Heat wok or large heavy deep nonstick skillet over medium-high heat until hot. Add 2 teaspoons of oil, swirling to coat wok. Sprinkle chicken with salt and add to wok. Stir-fry until cooked through, about 3 minutes. Transfer to plate.

2 Wipe out wok. Heat remaining 2 teaspoons oil in wok. Add ginger and stir-fry until fragrant, about 30 seconds. Add asparagus and water and cook, covered, until asparagus are crisp-tender, about 2 minutes.

3 Return chicken to wok along with black bean sauce. Stir-fry until chicken is heated through, about 1 minute longer.

 SmartPoints value per serving (1¼ cups): 230 Cal, 9 g Total Fat, 2 g Sat Fat, 698 mg Sod, 7 g Total Carb, 3 g Sugar, 3 g Fib, 29 g Prot.

Spicy blue cheese–chicken burgers

Serves 4

1	pound ground skinless chicken breast
2	scallions, thinly sliced
3	tablespoons plain dried bread crumbs
2	tablespoons hot pepper sauce, such as Frank's
½	teaspoon salt
¼	cup reduced-fat blue cheese dressing

1 Mix together chicken, scallions, bread crumbs, pepper sauce, and salt in medium bowl until combined well but not overmixed. With damp hands, shape mixture into 4 (4-inch) patties.

2 Spray ridged grill pan with nonstick spray and set over medium heat. Spray patties with nonstick spray, place in pan and cook until instant-read thermometer inserted into side of burger registers 165°F, about 5 minutes per side. Drizzle burgers with blue cheese dressing.

2 **SmartPoints value per serving** (1 burger and 1 tablespoon dressing): 200 Cal, 7 g Total Fat, 1 g Sat Fat, 706 mg Sod, 6 g Total Carb, 1 g Sugar, 0 g Fib, 27 g Prot.

Chicken kebabs
with pineapple

Chicken kebabs with pineapple

Serves 4

These kebabs were inspired by the Caribbean flavor combination of chicken, fresh pineapple, chile pepper, and lime. If you like heat, marinate the chicken overnight and, if you don't, 20 minutes will do the trick.

Grated zest and juice of 1 lime

1 tablespoon olive oil

1 jalapeño pepper, seeded and minced

2 garlic cloves, minced

½ teaspoon salt

¼ teaspoon black pepper

1 pound skinless boneless chicken breasts, cut into 1½-inch chunks

1½ cups fresh pineapple chunks

1 Combine lime juice, oil, jalapeño, garlic, salt, and black pepper in large zip-close plastic bag; add chicken. Squeeze out air and seal bag; turn to coat chicken. Refrigerate, turning bag occasionally, at least 20 minutes or up to overnight.

2 Spray grill rack with nonstick spray. Preheat grill to medium or prepare medium fire. Soak 4 (8 to 10-inch) wooden skewers in water at least 20 minutes.

3 Remove chicken from marinade; discard marinade. Thread chicken and pineapple alternately onto skewers. Spray kebabs with nonstick spray and place on grill rack. Grill, turning occasionally, until chicken is cooked through, about 7 minutes. Sprinkle with lime zest.

 SmartPoints value per serving (1 kebab): 209 Cal, 7 g Total Fat, 1 g Sat Fat, 343 mg Sod, 11 g Total Carb, 7 g Sugar, 1 g Fib, 26 g Prot.

Freestyle it

Enjoy the kebabs along with some grilled bell peppers for more color and flavor for 0 SmartPoints.

Turkey fingers with peach sauce

Serves 4

To serve the turkey fingers as an appetizer, thread each cooked finger onto a small decorative wooden skewer for easy dipping.

½ **cup peach or apricot all-fruit spread**

1 **teaspoon curry powder**

1 **(1-pound) piece skinless boneless turkey breast**

¾ **teaspoon salt**

¼ **teaspoon black pepper**

½ **cup unsweetened flaked coconut, chopped**

¼ **cup whole wheat panko bread crumbs**

1 Preheat oven to 425°F. Spray rimmed baking sheet with nonstick spray.

2 To make sauce, stir together ¼ cup of all-fruit spread and ½ teaspoon of curry powder in serving bowl. Set aside.

3 Cut turkey into 16 strips. Stir together remaining ¼ cup fruit spread, remaining ½ teaspoon curry powder, the salt, and pepper in medium bowl. Add turkey and toss until coated evenly.

4 Mix together coconut and panko on sheet of wax paper. Coat turkey strips, one at a time, in coconut mixture, lightly pressing so it adheres. Arrange turkey on prepared baking sheet in single layer and spray with nonstick spray. Bake until turkey fingers are golden and cooked through, about 15 minutes. Serve with reserved sauce.

 9 **SmartPoints value per serving** (4 turkey fingers and 1 tablespoon sauce): 305 Cal, 7 g Total Fat, 4 g Sat Fat, 592 mg Sod, 33 g Total Carb, 24 g Sugar, 2 g Fib, 28 g Prot.

Pan-glazed turkey tenderloin

Serves 4

Turkey tenderloin can sometimes be a bit more challenging to find in the meat case at a supermarket. So plan ahead and check with the butcher to see if it needs to be ordered.

⅓ **cup chicken broth**

¼ **cup apricot or peach all-fruit spread**

2 **tablespoons Dijon mustard**

1½ **teaspoons chopped fresh thyme or ½ teaspoon dried**

1 **tablespoon canola oil**

1 **(1-pound) piece skinless boneless turkey tenderloin**

½ **teaspoon salt**

¼ **teaspoon black pepper**

1 Stir together broth, fruit spread, mustard, and thyme in small bowl.

2 Heat oil in large skillet over medium-high heat. Sprinkle turkey with salt and pepper; add to skillet and cook, turning occasionally, until browned, about 5 minutes. Add apricot mixture and bring to boil. Reduce heat and simmer, covered, until instant-read thermometer inserted into center of turkey registers 165°F, about 12 minutes longer.

3 Transfer turkey to cutting board and let stand 5 minutes. Cut into 8 slices and serve with pan sauce.

 SmartPoints value per serving (2 slices turkey and 2 tablespoons sauce): 224 Cal, 5 g Total Fat, 1 g Sat Fat, 575 mg Sod, 15 g Total Carb, 10 g Sugar, 1 g Fib, 28 g Prot.

Freestyle it

Turn the tenderloin into a complete meal by serving it with a side of black beans sprinkled with diced red bell pepper and chopped fresh cilantro for 0 SmartPoints.

Grilled turkey saltimbocca

Grilled turkey saltimbocca

Serves 4

Saltimbocca, which means "jumps in the mouth" in Italian, refers to the tasty combination of flavors in this Roman specialty. Soaking the wooden skewers in water ensures that they won't char on the grill.

32	**pencil (thin) asparagus spears (about ¾ pound), trimmed**
4	**(¼-pound) turkey breast cutlets**
¼	**teaspoon salt**
¼	**teaspoon black pepper**
¼	**cup soft goat cheese**
12	**fresh sage leaves**
8	**(½-ounce) slices prosciutto**

1 Spray grill rack with nonstick spray. Preheat grill to medium or prepare medium fire. Soak 4 short wooden skewers in water at least 20 minutes.

2 Meanwhile, bring 1 inch of salted water to boil in large skillet. Add asparagus and cook, covered, until crisp-tender and bright green, about 2 minutes. With tongs, transfer to bowl of ice water and let cool about 2 minutes. Drain asparagus on double layer of paper towels and pat dry.

3 Place turkey cutlets between two pieces of plastic wrap. With meat mallet or rolling pin, lightly pound turkey to ¼-inch thickness. Remove top layer of plastic wrap and discard. Sprinkle turkey with salt and pepper. Spread 1 tablespoon goat cheese on each cutlet. Place 8 asparagus spears crosswise on each cutlet and roll up beginning with short side. Place 3 sage leaves on each roll and wrap in 2 slices of prosciutto. Secure each roll with skewer and lightly spray with nonstick spray.

4 Place rolls on grill rack and grill, covered, turning occasionally, until turkey is cooked through, about 12 minutes. Remove skewers before eating.

4 **SmartPoints value per serving** (1 turkey roll): 303 Cal, 13 g Total Fat, 5 g Sat Fat, 1,154 mg Sod, 5 g Total Carb, 2 g Sugar, 3 g Fib, 43 g Prot.

Hearty turkey-barley stew

Serves 6

This stew is perfect for a chilly night in the fall or winter. If you happen to have fresh parsley on hand, toss in a small handful—coarsely chopped or torn—along with a couple of shakes of Worcestershire sauce just before serving.

1	**ounce best-quality dried porcini mushrooms**
1½	**cups boiling water**
1	**tablespoon olive oil**
1	**(1-pound) piece skinless boneless turkey tenderloin, cut into ½-inch pieces**
3	**leeks (white and pale green parts only), thinly sliced**
1	**(32-ounce) carton chicken broth**
½	**cup pearl barley, rinsed**
¾	**teaspoon salt**
¼	**teaspoon black pepper**

1 Combine mushrooms and water in small bowl and let soak until mushrooms have softened, about 10 minutes. Pour mushrooms and mushroom liquid through paper towel–lined sieve set over small bowl. Reserve mushroom liquid and coarsely chop mushrooms.

2 Heat oil in large saucepan over medium-high heat. Add turkey and cook, stirring, until golden brown, about 8 minutes. Add leeks and cook, stirring, until softened, about 5 minutes. Add broth, barley, mushrooms and liquid, salt, and pepper and bring to boil. Reduce heat and simmer, covered, until barley is tender, about 30 minutes longer.

3  **SmartPoints value per serving** (1¼ cups): 231 Cal, 5 g Total Fat, 1 g Sat Fat, 846 mg Sod, 23 g Total Carb, 2 g Sugar, 4 g Fib, 24 g Prot.

Hoisin-marinated London broil

Serves 4

Hoisin sauce is a key ingredient in many Chinese dishes. This thick, dark, rich sauce is made from soy beans, fennel seeds, chiles, garlic, and vinegar.

¼ **cup hoisin sauce**

2 **large garlic cloves, minced**

1 **tablespoon grated peeled fresh ginger or refrigerated ginger paste**

1 **tablespoon rice vinegar**

1 **(1-pound) lean boneless sirloin steak, trimmed**

½ **teaspoon salt**

¼ **teaspoon black pepper**

1 Combine hoisin sauce, garlic, ginger, and vinegar in large zip-close plastic bag; add steak. Squeeze out air and seal bag; turn to coat steak. Refrigerate, turning bag occasionally, at least 4 hours or up to overnight.

2 Spray broiler rack with nonstick spray and preheat broiler.

3 Remove steak from marinade; discard marinade. Pat steak dry with paper towels and sprinkle with salt and pepper. Place on prepared broiler rack. Broil 5 inches from heat until instant-read thermometer inserted into side of steak registers 145°F, about 5 minutes per side. Transfer to cutting board and let stand 10 minutes. Cut steak across grain into 12 slices.

4 **SmartPoints value per serving** (3 slices steak): 187 Cal, 5 g Total Fat, 2 g Sat Fat, 614 mg Sod, 8 g Total Carb, 4 g Sugar, 0 g Fib, 26 g Prot.

Kielbasa and lentil stew

Serves 4

French green lentils, also known as Le Puy green lentils, are grown in the volcanic soil of the Auvergne region in France, which accounts for their unique nutty flavor.

1	**tablespoon olive oil**
¾	**pound turkey kielbasa, cut into 1-inch chunks**
1	**onion, thinly sliced**
1	**(14½-ounce) can diced tomatoes with Italian herbs**
1	**cup water**
1	**(15-ounce) can green lentils, drained, or 1½ cups vacuum-packed cooked green or brown lentils**
¼	**teaspoon salt**
⅛	**teaspoon black pepper**

1 Heat 2 teaspoons of oil in Dutch oven over medium-high heat. Add kielbasa and cook, stirring, until browned, about 5 minutes. With slotted spoon, transfer kielbasa to plate and set aside.

2 Heat remaining 1 teaspoon oil in same saucepan. Add onion and cook, stirring occasionally, until golden, about 8 minutes. Reduce heat to medium and add tomatoes. Pour water into empty tomato can and swirl can, then add tomato water to saucepan along with lentils, salt, and pepper. Bring to simmer and cook, covered, 10 minutes.

3 Stir kielbasa into lentil mixture and simmer, uncovered, until heated through and flavors are blended, about 5 minutes.

 SmartPoints value per serving (1¼ cups): 282 Cal, 11 g Total Fat, 3 g Sat Fat, 992 mg Sod, 25 g Total Carb, 5 g Sugar, 8 g Fib, 20 g Prot.

Kielbasa and
lentil stew

Coffee and chili–
crusted tenderloin

Coffee and chili-crusted tenderloin

Serves 4

Who doesn't like a nice thick slice or two of tender, juicy beef tenderloin, especially when it's been coated with a tasty layer of flavor? Here a dry rub of espresso powder, paprika, chili powder, salt, and pepper plays nicely against a thin layer of piquant Dijon.

1	**tablespoon olive oil**
1	**(1½-pound) lean beef tenderloin, trimmed and tied**
1	**tablespoon instant espresso powder, such as Medaglia d'Oro**
1½	**teaspoons paprika**
¾	**teaspoon chili powder**
½	**teaspoon salt**
½	**teaspoon black pepper**
2½	**teaspoons Dijon mustard**

1 Preheat oven to 425°F.

2 Heat oil in medium ovenproof skillet or heavy flameproof roasting pan over medium-high heat. Add beef and cook, turning, until browned on all sides, 4–5 minutes. Transfer beef to cutting board and let cool slightly. Remove string and discard. Set skillet aside (no need to wash).

3 Mix together espresso powder, paprika, chili powder, salt, and pepper in cup. Brush mustard all over beef but not on ends. Sprinkle two-thirds of coffee mixture over mustard, gently patting so it adheres. Sprinkle beef with remaining coffee mixture.

4 Return beef to skillet and roast in oven until instant-read thermometer inserted into center of beef registers 145°F, about 25 minutes. Transfer beef to cutting board, cover loosely with foil, and let stand 10 minutes. Cut into 8 thick slices and serve drizzled with any accumulated meat juices.

6 **SmartPoints value per serving** (2 slices tenderloin): 288 Cal, 14 g Total Fat, 4 g Sat Fat, 435 mg Sod, 1 g Total Carb, 0 g Sugar, 1 g Fib, 38 g Prot.

Braised Italian-style pork chops

Serves 4

1	**tablespoon olive oil**
4	**(¼-pound) lean boneless center-cut pork loin chops, trimmed**
¾	**teaspoon salt**
¼	**teaspoon black pepper**
1	**onion, chopped**
1	**red or green bell pepper, diced**
2	**large garlic cloves, thinly sliced**
1	**cup spicy tomato sauce, such as arrabiatta**

1 Heat oil in large heavy nonstick skillet over medium-high heat. Sprinkle pork with salt and black pepper and place in skillet. Cook until browned, about 3 minutes per side. Transfer to plate.

2 Reduce heat to medium. Add onion, bell pepper, and garlic to skillet and cook, stirring, until vegetables begin to soften, about 3 minutes. Return pork chops to skillet and pour tomato sauce over. Simmer, covered, until instant-read thermometer inserted into side of chop registers 145°F, about 5 minutes.

6 **SmartPoints value per serving** (1 pork chop and ⅔ cup sauce): 258 Cal, 13 g Total Fat, 3 g Sat Fat, 720 mg Sod, 9 g Total Carb, 5 g Sugar, 2 g Fib, 25 g Prot.

Freestyle it
Grilled slices of unpeeled eggplant would play nicely with the flavors of this dish. And there's enough tomato sauce for spooning over the eggplant if you like.

Grilled Swiss chard and tomato pizzas

Serves 8

1 (¾-pound) bunch Swiss chard, tough stems removed and leaves cut into large pieces

1 red onion, cut into ¼-inch rounds

1 pound refrigerated pizza dough, at room temperature

4 large plum tomatoes, cut crosswise into ¼-inch slices

¼ teaspoon black pepper

1 cup shredded part-skim mozzarella cheese

1 Spray grill rack with nonstick spray. Preheat grill to medium-high or prepare medium-high fire.

2 Spray Swiss chard and onion with olive oil nonstick spray and place on grill rack. Grill, turning, until vegetables are lightly browned and tender, about 3 minutes for chard and 5 minutes for onion. Transfer vegetables to cutting board as they are done; coarsely chop. Keep grill on.

3 Divide dough into 4 equal pieces. On lightly floured work surface with floured rolling pin, roll each piece of dough into thin round. Lightly spray tops of dough rounds with nonstick spray. Place dough rounds, sprayed-side down, on grill rack and grill until golden brown on bottom, about 2 minutes.

4 With tongs, transfer pizza crusts to cutting board or baking peel and turn cooked-side up. Spray crusts with nonstick spray and top evenly with chard, onion, and tomatoes; sprinkle with pepper and top with mozzarella. Return pizzas to grill and grill, covered, until golden brown on bottom and cheese has melted, about 3 minutes. Cut each pizza in half.

6 **SmartPoints value per serving** (½ pizza): 221 Cal, 7 g Total Fat, 3 g Sat Fat, 564 mg Sod, 29 g Total Carb, 5 g Sugar, 1 g Fib, 11 g Prot.

Cherry and thyme–stuffed pork

Serves 8

Serve this elegant yet easy-to-prepare pork roast the next time you want to dazzle guests. The roast can be stuffed and refrigerated up to 6 hours ahead. Leave it out at room temperature about 20 minutes before roasting.

⅓ **cup dried cherries, chopped**

½ **cup cherry all-fruit spread**

3 **tablespoons plain dried bread crumbs**

4 **teaspoons chopped fresh thyme**

1 **(1½-pound) lean boneless center-cut pork loin, trimmed**

¾ **teaspoon salt**

¼ **teaspoon black pepper**

1 Preheat oven to 400°F. Set rack in roasting pan and spray rack and pan with nonstick spray.

2 To make stuffing, combine cherries with enough boiling water to cover in small bowl. Let cherries soak until softened, about 10 minutes; drain well. Stir in ¼ cup of fruit spread, the bread crumbs, and thyme until mixed well.

3 With long thin knife, cut pork lengthwise in half, cutting about three-fourths through and opening pork up like a book. Place pork, cut-side down, between two sheets of wax paper. With meat mallet or rolling pin, gently pound pork to ½-inch thickness. Remove top sheet of wax paper and sprinkle pork with salt and pepper. Turn pork over and spoon cherry mixture down along center. Roll pork up lengthwise to enclose filling and tie in 4 or 5 places with kitchen string.

4 Place pork on prepared rack and roast 45 minutes Brush with 1 tablespoon of fruit spread. Roast until instant-read thermometer inserted into center of pork registers 145°F, about 15 minutes longer, brushing 3 times with remaining fruit spread. Transfer pork to cutting board and let stand 10 minutes. Cut off string and discard. Cut pork into 24 (¼-inch) slices.

4 **SmartPoints value per serving** (3 slices pork): 163 Cal, 4 g Total Fat, 2 g Sat Fat, 292 mg Sod, 13 g Total Carb, 6 g Sugar, 4 g Fib, 19 g Prot.

Cherry and
thyme-stuffed pork

Butterflied lamb with couscous salad

Serves 4

This recipe showcases the delicate flavor of spring lamb. Give the grill pan enough time to get good and hot, ensuring the lamb gets a crust on the outside while remaining tender and juicy on the inside.

1	**cup whole wheat couscous**
1	**tablespoon extra-virgin olive oil**
1	**tomato, cut into small dice**
⅓	**cup chopped fresh flat-leaf parsley**
1½	**teaspoons salt**
½	**teaspoon black pepper**
1	**(1-pound) lean boneless leg of lamb, butterflied and trimmed**

1 Cook couscous according to package directions. Transfer to serving bowl and let cool slightly; fluff with fork. Drizzle with oil and stir in tomato, parsley, ½ teaspoon of salt, and ¼ teaspoon of pepper.

2 Meanwhile, spray ridged grill pan with nonstick spray and set over medium-high heat until hot. Sprinkle lamb with remaining 1 teaspoon salt and ¼ teaspoon pepper. Place lamb in pan and cook, turning once, until instant-read thermometer inserted into center of lamb registers 145°F, about 12 minutes.

3 Transfer lamb to cutting board and let stand 10 minutes. Cut across grain into 12 slices. Serve with couscous.

 SmartPoints value per serving (3 slices lamb and about 1 cup couscous): 334 Cal, 8 g Total Fat, 2 g Sat Fat, 968 mg Sod, 35 g Total Carb, 4 g Sugar, 6 g Fib, 30 g Prot.

Add this
Serve our tasty, easy Lemony Fennel and Radicchio (page 137) alongside for an additional 1 SmartPoints per serving.

Butterflied
lamb with
couscous salad

Spaghettini with limas and tomatoes

Serves 4

In the spring, make this dish even more delicious by substituting fresh fava beans for the lima beans. To get 2 cups of beans you'll need about 2 pounds of pods.

1 tablespoon extra-virgin olive oil

2 (14½-ounce) cans diced fire-roasted tomatoes with garlic

2 cups frozen baby lima beans

½ teaspoon black pepper

½ pound spaghettini (thin spaghetti)

⅔ cup torn fresh basil

1 Heat oil in large deep skillet over medium-high heat. Add tomatoes, lima beans, and pepper and bring to boil. Reduce heat and simmer, covered, stirring occasionally, 20 minutes.

2 Meanwhile, cook spaghettini according to package directions. Drain spaghettini and add to tomato mixture, tossing until mixed well. Transfer to serving bowl. Add basil and toss until combined.

 SmartPoints value per serving (1½ cups): 385 Cal, 5 g Total Fat, 1 g Sat Fat, 333 mg Sod, 70 g Total Carb, 8 g Sugar, 9 g Fib, 15 g Prot.

Freestyle it

Begin your meal with a mixed baby greens salad dressed with fresh lemon juice, salt, and pepper.

Stir-fried tofu with scallions

Serves 4

Tofu is akin to a sponge, as it happily absorbs the flavors of other ingredients. Since tofu is so mild-flavored, tossing it with black bean sauce, which has a complex flavor profile works like a charm.

1   **(14-ounce) package extra-firm tofu, drained**

2   **bunches small scallions (white and light green parts only), trimmed**

2   **teaspoons canola oil**

¼   **teaspoon black pepper**

2   **teaspoons Asian (dark) sesame oil**

2   **orange bell peppers, cut into 1-inch pieces**

⅓   **cup water**

⅓   **cup black bean sauce**

1 Gently press tofu between several layers of paper towels to remove excess water. Cut into 1-inch cubes. Set aside.

2 Cut 2 scallions lengthwise in half and then into long, thin shreds. Set aside. Cut remaining scallions crosswise into thirds. Set aside.

3 Heat wok or large heavy deep nonstick skillet over medium-high heat until drop of water sizzles in wok. Add canola oil, swirling to coat pan. Add tofu, sprinkle with ⅛ teaspoon of black pepper and cook, turning tofu occasionally, until golden, about 5 minutes. Transfer to plate.

4 Increase heat to high. Add sesame oil to wok along with bell peppers, scallion pieces, and remaining ⅛ teaspoon black pepper. Stir-fry until bell peppers are lightly charred, about 4 minutes. Reduce heat to low and stir in water and black bean sauce. Cook, stirring, until heated through, about 2 minutes. Gently stir in tofu and shredded scallions.

3 **SmartPoints value per serving** (about 1 cup): 201 Cal, 12 g Total Fat, 2 g Sat Fat, 481 mg Sod, 12 g Total Carb, 4 g Sugar, 4 g Fib, 14 g Prot.

Polenta "pizza" margherita

Serves 4

Creamy, rich ricotta cheese is unusual in that it is made from the whey leftover from cheese making.

1   **(1-pound) tube plain fat-free polenta, cut into ¼-inch rounds**

¾   **cup part-skim ricotta cheese**

¼   **cup grated Parmesan cheese**

¼   **teaspoon black pepper**

3   **plum tomatoes, thinly sliced into rounds and patted dry with paper towels**

½   **cup shredded part-skim mozzarella cheese**

1 Preheat broiler. Spray 10-inch pizza pan or large baking sheet with nonstick spray.

2 Place 1 slice of polenta in center of prepared pan. Arrange remaining slices of polenta in two concentric circles around first slice, slightly overlapping polenta to form 10-inch polenta round. Lightly spray polenta with nonstick spray. Broil 5 inches from heat until lightly browned and heated through, about 8 minutes.

3 Meanwhile, stir together ricotta, Parmesan, and pepper in small bowl.

4 Arrange tomato slices on top of polenta and dollop with ricotta-Parmesan mixture; sprinkle with mozzarella. Broil until tomatoes are heated through and mozzarella has melted, about 4 minutes. Cut into 4 wedges.

7 **SmartPoints value per serving** (1 wedge): 214 Cal, 8 g Total Fat, 5 g Sat Fat, 577 mg Sod, 22 g Total Carb, 2 g Sugar, 2 g Fib, 13 g Prot.

Polenta "pizza"
margherita

Marinated tofu and
vegetable kebabs

Marinated tofu and vegetable kebabs

Serves 4

1   (14-ounce) package extra-firm tofu, drained
2   zucchini, each cut into 12 (½-inch) slices
1   red bell pepper, cut into 1-inch pieces
1   red onion, quartered and separated into 16 pieces
¼   cup teriyaki sauce
⅛   teaspoon black pepper

1 Line broiler pan with foil and spray broiler rack with nonstick spray.

2 Gently press tofu between several layers of paper towels to remove excess water. Cut into 24 (1-inch) cubes.

3 Thread tofu alternately with zucchini, bell pepper, and onion onto 8 (10- to 12-inch) metal skewers (if using wooden skewers, soak them in water at least 20 minutes to prevent charring).

4 Place skewers on baking sheet. Brush on all sides with some of teriyaki sauce. Let stand about 30 minutes, turning and brushing with sauce once or twice more.

5 Meanwhile, preheat broiler to high.

6 Transfer kebabs to prepared broiler rack. Broil about 4 inches from heat, turning several times, until vegetables have started to soften and tofu has browned, about 12 minutes. Sprinkle with black pepper.

1 **SmartPoints value per serving** (2 kebabs): 147 Cal, 6 g Total Fat, 1 g Sat Fat, 703 mg Sod, 13 g Total Carb, 7 g Sugar, 4 g Fib, 14 g Prot.

Freestyle it
Put the cooked tofu and vegetables onto Boston lettuce leaves and enjoy as wraps.

Chapter 5
Eat your "greens"

Roasted Brussels sprouts with walnuts

Serves 8

Tender sweet shallots and perfectly cooked Brussels sprouts are a welcome texture counterpoint to the crunchy toasted walnuts.

2	**pints Brussels sprouts, trimmed and halved or quartered if large**
4	**large shallots, thickly sliced**
2	**tablespoons olive oil**
½	**teaspoon salt**
¼	**teaspoon black pepper**
4	**slices center-cut bacon, crisp-cooked and torn into ½-inch pieces**
¼	**cup walnuts, chopped and toasted**

1 Preheat oven to 450°F.

2 Combine Brussels sprouts and shallots on large rimmed baking sheet. Drizzle with oil and sprinkle with salt and pepper, tossing until coated evenly. Spread to form even layer. Roast until Brussels sprouts and shallots are tender, about 20 minutes, stirring once or twice.

3 Transfer Brussels sprouts mixture to serving bowl. Add bacon and walnuts and toss until mixed well.

3 **SmartPoints value per serving** (½ cup): 118 Cal, 8 g Total Fat, 1 g Sat Fat, 256 mg Sod, 9 g Total Carb, 3 g Sugar, 3 g Fib, 5 g Prot.

**Roasted Brussels sprouts
with walnuts**

Sesame broccoli

Serves 4

This recipe is delicious as is, but if you want a flavorful vegetable to add, think red bell peppers, which are high in vitamin C. Thinly slice a large red bell pepper and add it to the steamer basket along with the broccoli in step 1.

4	**cups small broccoli florets**
2	**tablespoons soy sauce**
1	**tablespoon honey**
2	**teaspoons Asian (dark) sesame oil**
2	**teaspoons toasted sesame seeds**
1	**garlic clove, crushed through a press**

1 Put broccoli in steamer basket and set in large saucepan over 1 inch of boiling water. Cover and steam until broccoli is crisp-tender, about 4 minutes.

2 Meanwhile, stir together soy sauce, honey, sesame oil, sesame seeds, and garlic in serving bowl. Add broccoli and toss until mixed well.

SmartPoints value per serving (1 cup): 70 Cal, 3 g Total Fat, 0 g Sat Fat, 455 mg Sod, 9 g Total Carb, 5 g Sugar, 2 g Fib, 3 g Prot.

Braised red cabbage and pears

Serves 6

Order a side of *blaukraut* in a German or German-American restaurant and you'll get a bowl of braised red cabbage. Meltingly tender with a subtle sweet-and-sour edge, it's the perfect hearty accompaniment to game, poultry, or pork.

1   **small red cabbage (about 1½ pounds), quartered, cored, and thinly sliced**

2   **ripe Bosc or Bartlett pears, peeled, cored, quartered, and thickly sliced crosswise**

1   **small onion, thinly sliced**

2   **tablespoons cider vinegar**

2   **tablespoons water**

½   **teaspoon salt**

¼   **teaspoon black pepper**

1   **tablespoon unsalted butter, cut into small pieces**

1   Combine cabbage, pears, onion, vinegar, water, salt, and pepper in large pot and set over medium heat. Cook, covered, until cabbage is wilted, about 10 minutes.

2   Reduce heat to medium-low and cook, stirring occasionally, until cabbage is very tender, about 30 minutes, adding a couple tablespoons of water if mixture seems dry. Stir in butter until melted.

1   **SmartPoints value per serving** (¾ cup): 89 Cal, 2 g Total Fat, 1 g Sat Fat, 222 mg Sod, 18 g Total Carb, 10 g Sugar, 4 g Fib, 2 g Prot.

Freestyle it

Serve this delicious sweet-and-sour braised cabbage dish alongside 0 SmartPoints grilled or broiled skinless boneless chicken breasts or salmon fillets. The recipe will no longer be vegetarian.

Very French
grated
carrot salad

Very French grated carrot salad

Serves 4

Carrot salad, *carottes rapées,* can be found in just about every take-out shop in France. The key to success is lying the carrots on their sides and using the thinnest shredding blade your food processor has.

¾   **pound large carrots**

1   **tablespoon finely chopped fresh flat-leaf parsley**

1   **tablespoon lemon juice**

2   **teaspoons Dijon mustard**

¼   **teaspoon salt**

⅛   **teaspoon black pepper**

1   **tablespoon plus 1 teaspoon extra-virgin olive oil**

1 Cut carrots to fit horizontally in feed tube of food processor. Stack carrots in feed tube and grate using thin shredding blade (or use large holes of box grater) to create long, thin strands (you need about 3 cups). Transfer carrots to salad bowl and add parsley.

2 To make dressing, whisk together lemon juice, mustard, salt, and pepper in small bowl. Slowly whisk in oil in thin, steady steam.

3 Pour dressing over carrot mixture and toss until mixed well. Let stand, covered, at room temperature up to 3 hours.

1 **SmartPoints value per serving** (½ cup): 77 Cal, 5 g Total Fat, 1 g Sat Fat, 232 mg Sod, 9 g Total Carb, 4 g Sugar, 2 g Fib, 1 g Prot.

Carrot-horseradish puree

Serves 4

Here carrots are cooked until tender then whirled in a food processor until silky smooth. Butter adds a touch of creamy richness, while bottled horseradish gives it an unexpected note of heat. Serve this at your next Thanksgiving dinner.

1½ **pounds carrots, very thinly sliced**

1 **tablespoon reduced-fat (2%) milk**

1 **tablespoon butter**

1 **tablespoon prepared horseradish**

½ **teaspoon salt or to taste**

¼ **teaspoon black pepper**

1 Bring large saucepan of water to boil. Add carrots and return to boil. Reduce heat and simmer, covered, until carrots are very tender, about 15 minutes. Drain well.

2 Combine carrots, milk, and butter in food processor and process until very smooth. Transfer to serving bowl and stir in horseradish, salt, and pepper.

1 **SmartPoints value per serving** (about ½ cup): 51 Cal, 3 g Total Fat, 2 g Sat Fat, 346 mg Sod, 6 g Total Carb, 3 g Sugar, 2 g Fib, 1 g Prot.

Cauliflower with lemon and cumin

Serves 4

1	**small head cauliflower, cut into small florets**
2	**teaspoons olive oil**
½	**teaspoon ground cumin**
½	**teaspoon salt**
¼	**teaspoon black pepper**

Grated zest and juice of ½ lemon

1	**garlic clove, minced**

1 Preheat oven to 450°F.

2 Put cauliflower on large rimmed baking sheet. Drizzle with oil and sprinkle with cumin, salt, and pepper. Toss until coated evenly; spread to form even layer.

3 Roast 15 minutes, stirring once. Sprinkle cauliflower with lemon zest and juice and garlic, tossing to coat. Roast until cauliflower is tender, about 3 minutes longer.

 SmartPoints value per serving (1 cup): 42 Cal, 2 g Total Fat, 0 g Sat Fat, 312 mg Sod, 5 g Total Carb, 2 g Sugar, 2 g Fib, 2 g Prot.

Freestyle it

Our vegetable side dish, brightly flavored with fresh lemon juice and zest, would pair well with 0 SmartPoints grilled or broiled chicken breasts, salmon steaks, shrimp, or calamari.

Whole roasted
tandoori cauliflower

Whole roasted tandoori cauliflower

Serves 6

Don't tell anyone how easy it was to prepare this vegetable showstopper! Brilliant yellow on the outside and perfectly tender on the inside, cauliflower never tasted this good. If you like, roast it up to several hours ahead, then reheat in the microwave.

1	**large head cauliflower**
⅔	**cup plain fat-free Greek yogurt**
2	**garlic cloves, minced**
1½	**teaspoons tandoori seasoning**
½	**teaspoon salt**
2	**tablespoons chopped fresh cilantro**

1 Preheat oven to 400°F. Spray 9-inch pie plate or small shallow baking dish with nonstick spray.

2 Remove outer leaves and core from cauliflower and discard, keeping head intact. Place cauliflower in prepared baking dish, core-side down. Whisk together yogurt, garlic, tandoori seasoning, and salt in small bowl. Spread evenly over cauliflower.

3 Roast until small knife inserted into center of cauliflower goes in easily and topping is browned, about 1 hour 30 minutes, rotating dish once or twice during roasting so cauliflower cooks evenly.

4 Let cauliflower stand 10 minutes to cool slightly. Sprinkle with cilantro and cut into 6 wedges.

0 **SmartPoints value per serving** (1 wedge): 52 Cal, 0 g Total Fat, 0 g Sat Fat, 249 mg Sod, 9 g Total Carb, 4 g Sugar, 4 g Fib, 5 g Prot.

Grilled Parmesan corn on the cob

Serves 8

This classic Mexican street food can take the heat. Add 1 or 2 teaspoons of chili powder (pictured) or a pinch of cayenne to the mayonnaise mixture.

8   **ears of corn**

⅔   **cup reduced-fat mayonnaise**

¼   **cup chopped fresh cilantro**

Grated zest and juice of 1 lime

¼   **cup grated Parmesan cheese**

1 Preheat grill to medium-high or prepare medium-high fire.

2 Gently pull husks down from corn and remove silk. Pull husks back over corn.

3 Wrap each ear of corn in sheet of heavy foil. Place on grill rack and grill, turning corn occasionally, until very tender, about 15 minutes.

4 Meanwhile, mix together mayonnaise, cilantro, and lime zest and juice in cup.

5 Remove husks from corn, brush all over with mayonnaise mixture, and sprinkle with Parmesan.

 SmartPoints value per serving (1 ear of corn): 162 Cal, 7 g Total Fat, 1 g Sat Fat, 223 mg Sod, 25 g Total Carb, 6 g Sugar, 3 g Fib, 5 g Prot.

Grilled Parmesan
corn on the cob

"Creamed" corn

Serves 4

Typically creamed corn is made by cooking corn kernels with a little sugar and a good amount of heavy cream. But if you grate the corn from some of the ears, you end up with creamed corn that is laden with fresh corn flavor.

6	**ears of corn, husks and silk removed**
2	**teaspoons olive oil**
1	**small onion, finely chopped**
½	**cup vegetable broth**
¼	**teaspoon salt**
⅛	**teaspoon black pepper**
1	**tablespoon water**
2	**teaspoons cornstarch**

1 Hold box grater over large bowl and using large holes, grate corn from 4 ears, letting milky liquid fall into bowl. Standing remaining ears of corn, one at a time, on cutting board, slice down length of ears to remove corn, cutting as close to cob as possible. Coarsely chop kernels and stir into corn liquid. Set aside.

2 Heat oil in medium saucepan over medium heat. Add onion and cook, stirring, until softened, about 5 minutes. Stir in corn mixture, broth, salt, and pepper and bring to boil. Reduce heat and simmer, covered, stirring occasionally, until corn is tender, about 10 minutes.

3 Meanwhile, whisk together water and cornstarch in cup until smooth. Stir into corn and cook, stirring constantly, until mixture is slightly thickened, about 1 minute.

1 **SmartPoints value per serving** (about ¾ cup): 181 Cal, 5 g Total Fat, 1 g Sat Fat, 231 mg Sod, 36 g Total Carb, 8 g Sugar, 4 g Fib, 6 g Prot.

Coconut-cumin green beans

Serves 4

Did you know that green beans are also called snap beans? This well-deserved name reflects the sound the beans make when their ends are snapped (broken) off to trim them.

1	**pound green beans, trimmed**
2	**teaspoons canola oil**
⅓	**cup unsweetened flaked coconut**
½	**teaspoon cumin seeds, crushed**
½	**teaspoon salt**
⅛	**teaspoon black pepper**

1 Bring medium saucepan of water to boil over high heat. Add green beans and cook, covered, until crisp-tender, about 3 minutes. Drain and cover to keep warm.

2 Meanwhile, heat oil in large skillet over medium heat. Add coconut and cumin and cook, stirring constantly, until coconut is toasted, about 2 minutes. Add green beans, salt, and pepper and cook, stirring constantly, until heated through, about 1 minute longer.

3 **SmartPoints value per serving** (generous ¾ cup): 87 Cal, 5 g Total Fat, 3 g Sat Fat, 304 mg Sod, 9 g Total Carb, 2 g Sugar, 5 g Fib, 2 g Prot.

**Lemony fennel
and radicchio**

Lemony fennel and radicchio

Serves 4

Italians love their fennel for its anise (licorice) flavor. Also known as Florence fennel and finocchio, it is as much at home in salads as it is roasted, braised, or grilled. If the fennel comes with its feathery fronds, chop them and scatter over the finished dish.

2	**fennel bulbs, trimmed and thinly sliced lengthwise**
1	**tablespoon olive oil**
¼	**teaspoon salt**
⅛	**teaspoon black pepper**
¼	**cup water**
1	**cup thinly sliced radicchio**
2	**tablespoons chopped fresh flat-leaf parsley**
1	**teaspoon grated lemon zest**
1	**tablespoon lemon juice**

1 Put fennel in large bowl. Add oil and toss until coated evenly. Transfer fennel to large nonstick skillet; sprinkle with salt and pepper and set over medium heat. Cook, stirring, 1 minute. Add water and cook, covered, until fennel begins to soften, about 3 minutes longer.

2 Uncover skillet and increase heat to medium-high. Cook, stirring, until most of water has evaporated and fennel is tender, about 2 minutes. Remove skillet from heat and stir in radicchio, parsley, and lemon zest and juice.

 SmartPoints value per serving (1 cup): 71 Cal, 4 g Total Fat, 0 g Sat Fat, 210 mg Sod, 10 g Total Carb, 0 g Sugar, 4 g Fib, 2 g Prot.

**Peas with
crispy prosciutto**

Peas with crispy prosciutto

Serves 4

2   teaspoons olive oil

2   (½-ounce) slices prosciutto, trimmed and torn into small pieces or chopped

1   large shallot, halved lengthwise and thinly sliced

2½ cups frozen peas (about 12 ounces)

⅓   cup water

⅛   teaspoon salt

⅛   teaspoon black pepper

1   tablespoon thinly sliced fresh mint

1   Heat 1 teaspoon of oil in medium heavy nonstick skillet over medium-high heat. Add prosciutto and cook, stirring often, until crisp, about 3 minutes. With slotted spoon, transfer prosciutto to paper towels to drain.

2   Add remaining 1 teaspoon oil to skillet. Add shallot and cook, stirring, until softened but not browned, about 2 minutes. Stir in peas, water, salt, and pepper and bring to boil. Reduce heat and simmer until peas are tender and most of water has evaporated, about 4 minutes.

3   Remove skillet from heat and stir in mint. Transfer to serving bowl and crumble prosciutto on top.

 SmartPoints value per serving (about ½ cup): 125 Cal, 4 g Total Fat, 1 g Sat Fat, 414 mg Sod, 15 g Total Carb, 6 g Sugar, 5 g Fib, 8 g Prot.

**Rosemary-roasted
radishes**

Rosemary-roasted radishes

Serves 4

The green tops of radishes are a welcome change from other more common greens. Firm textured with a slight bite, they are a good-for-you veggie that tastes great cooked as well as raw in a salad.

2   **large bunches of radishes with green tops attached (about 20)**

1   **tablespoon olive oil**

2   **teaspoons chopped fresh rosemary**

½   **teaspoon salt**

¼   **teaspoon black pepper**

1   **teaspoon lemon juice**

1 Set rack in upper third of oven. Preheat oven to 425°F.

2 Separate radishes and green tops; set greens aside. Trim radishes and cut lengthwise in half.

3 Combine radishes, oil, rosemary, salt, and pepper in large bowl, tossing until coated. Transfer to large rimmed baking sheet, leaving about 1 teaspoon rosemary mixture in bowl. Roast radishes 20 minutes.

4 Meanwhile, rinse radish greens under cool water to remove any grit or sand, discarding any wilted or yellowing leaves. Tear any large leaves in half and trim any tough stems. Add greens to rosemary mixture in bowl and toss until coated. Remove radishes from oven and add greens, tossing until combined. Roast until greens are wilted and radishes are tender, about 5 minutes. Drizzle with lemon juice.

1   **SmartPoints value per serving** (generous ⅔ cup): 38 Cal, 3 g Total Fat, 0 g Sat Fat, 308 mg Sod, 2 g Total Carb, 1 g Sugar, 1 g Fib, 0 g Prot.

Stir-fried garlic spinach

Serves 4

There are three types of spinach in supermarkets: baby spinach, curly spinach, and flat spinach, which is sold by the bunch. Flat spinach is more delicate than curly spinach and not as pricey as baby spinach, making it a great choice.

2   teaspoons canola oil
2   large garlic cloves, minced
10 ounces flat spinach, trimmed
1   tablespoon soy sauce
1   tablespoon rice vinegar
⅛   teaspoon black pepper

Heat wok or large heavy deep nonstick skillet over high heat until drop of water sizzles in wok. Add oil and swirl to coat pan. Add garlic and stir-fry just until fragrant, about 15 seconds. Add spinach, soy sauce, vinegar, and pepper and stir-fry just until spinach is wilted, about 2 minutes.

 SmartPoints value per serving (about ⅓ cup): 42 Cal, 3 g Total Fat, 0 g Sat Fat, 274 mg Sod, 4 g Total Carb, 0 g Sugar, 2 g Fib, 2 g Prot.

Roasted acorn squash with thyme

Serves 4

2	acorn squash
1	tablespoon olive oil
1½	tablespoons chopped fresh thyme
½	teaspoon kosher salt
¼	teaspoon black pepper

1 Preheat oven to 400°F. Spray large rimmed baking sheet with olive oil nonstick spray.

2 Using a long serrated knife, halve squash through stem end. With spoon, scrape out seeds and cut each squash half in half to make total of 8 wedges. Place squash, skin-side down, on prepared baking sheet. Brush with oil and sprinkle with thyme, salt, and pepper.

3 Roast until squash is tender and golden brown along edges, about 40 minutes.

 SmartPoints value per serving (2 wedges): 118 Cal, 4 g Total Fat, 1 g Sat Fat, 248 mg Sod, 23 g Total Carb, 0 g Sugar, 3 g Fib, 2 g Prot.

Try this

Roasted acorn squash is a made-for-fall vegetable. Enjoy it at your next Thanksgiving dinner. The recipe is easily doubled or even tripled. Roast the squash, in batches if needed, early in the day, and re-warm in a 200°F oven once you've taken out the turkey.

Tomato and garlic-stuffed peppers

Serves 4

Pretty as a picture and as flavorful as can be, these hardly-any-fuss stuffed peppers are sure to become part of your go-to recipe repertoire. Get creative and use assorted-color peppers, such as orange, yellow, purple, or green, for a carnival of colors.

4	**red bell peppers**
48	**cherry tomatoes (about 1½ pounds)**
2	**garlic cloves, thinly sliced**
3	**anchovies (packed in oil), thinly sliced and 2½ teaspoons oil reserved**
2	**large fresh rosemary or thyme sprigs**
⅛	**teaspoon salt**
⅛	**teaspoon black pepper**

1 Preheat oven to 375°F. Line large rimmed baking sheet with foil and spray with nonstick spray.

2 Cut bell peppers lengthwise in half being sure to cut through middle of each stem to keep intact. Carefully remove cores and seeds and discard. Place peppers, cut-side up, on prepared baking sheet.

3 Tightly fit about 6 whole cherry tomatoes into each pepper half. Tuck garlic and anchovies into each half, dividing evenly. Break rosemary sprigs into little sprigs and tuck between tomatoes. Drizzle reserved anchovy oil over tomatoes and sprinkle with salt and pepper.

4 Roast until bell peppers are tender and browned along edges and tomatoes are softened, about 40 minutes.

 SmartPoints value per serving (2 stuffed pepper halves): 86 Cal, 4 g Total Fat, 1 g Sat Fat, 192 mg Sod, 12 g Total Carb, 7 g Sugar, 4 g Fib, 3 g Prot.

Tomato and garlic-stuffed peppers

Quick-cook fresh tomato sauce

Serves 8

Got an abundance of tomatoes in your garden? Pick the ripest ones you can find and use them here. Sauce made with fresh tomatoes has a delicate flavor, which is especially welcome during the warmer months.

3	**tablespoons olive oil**
1	**small onion, chopped**
4	**large garlic cloves**
2	**pounds ripe tomatoes, cored and diced, juice reserved**
1	**tablespoon tomato paste**
2	**teaspoons kosher salt**
¼	**teaspoon black pepper**
½	**cup chopped fresh basil**

1 Heat oil in large saucepan over medium heat. Add onion and cook, stirring, until softened, about 5 minutes. Add garlic and cook, stirring frequently, until fragrant, about 30 seconds.

2 Add tomatoes with their juice, tomato paste, salt, and pepper; cook, stirring, until tomatoes break down and begin to soften, about 4 minutes. Stir in basil.

 SmartPoints value per serving (½ cup): 73 Cal, 5 g Total Fat, 1 g Sat Fat, 505 mg Sod, 6 g Total Carb, 4 g Sugar, 2 g Fib, 1 g Prot.

Grilled zucchini with feta and lemon

Serves 6

Take advantage of the abundance and low price of zucchini at the height of summer in your local farmers' market. This easy dish is great for serving a crowd.

½ **cup crumbled reduced-fat feta cheese**

3 **scallions, thinly sliced**

1 **tablespoon extra-virgin olive oil**

Grated zest of 1 lemon

4 **(6-ounce) zucchini, ends trimmed**

½ **teaspoon kosher salt**

¼ **teaspoon black pepper**

1 Spray grill rack with nonstick spray. Preheat grill to high or prepare hot fire.

2 Meanwhile, stir together feta, scallions, oil, and lemon zest in small bowl; set aside.

3 Cut zucchini lengthwise in half and cut each half into 4 or 5 pieces. Put zucchini into large bowl and lightly spray with olive oil nonstick spray. Sprinkle with salt and pepper, tossing to coat.

4 Place zucchini on grill rack and grill, turning, until well-marked and tender, about 6 minutes. Transfer zucchini to platter or serving bowl and sprinkle with feta mixture.

1 **SmartPoints value per serving** (about 5 pieces zucchini and heaping 1 tablespoon feta mixture): 63 Cal, 4 g Total Fat, 1 g Sat Fat, 294 mg Sod, 53 g Total Carb, 3 g Sugar, 1 g Fib, 4 g Prot.

Add this

A small handful of thinly sliced or torn fresh mint leaves would make a flavorful addition to this tasty vegetable dish.

Three-vegetable tian

Three-vegetable tian

Serves 4

4   **small fresh thyme sprigs plus 1½ teaspoons finely chopped thyme**

2   **tablespoons plus 1 teaspoon extra-virgin olive oil**

2   **(5-ounce) evenly shaped slender eggplant, trimmed and cut into ¼-inch rounds**

3   **(¼-pound) plum tomatoes, cut into ¼-inch slices**

1   **large zucchini (about 10 ounces), cut into ¼-inch slices**

½   **teaspoon salt**

¼   **teaspoon black pepper**

1 Preheat oven to 400°F. Spray 7½ x 10-inch rectangular or oval shallow baking dish with olive oil nonstick spray. Scatter thyme sprigs in bottom of dish.

2 Mix together oil and chopped thyme in cup. Arrange eggplant, tomato, and zucchini slices in single layer on large baking sheet or on large sheet of foil. Brush thyme oil over vegetables and sprinkle with salt and pepper.

3 Stand vegetables in tight rows in prepared baking dish, alternating vegetables. Spray with nonstick spray.

4 Bake until vegetables are tender and lightly browned along edges, about 50 minutes. Let stand at least 5 minutes to allow flavors to blend. Serve hot, warm, or at room temperature.

2   **SmartPoints value per serving** (¾ cup): 118 Cal, 9 g Total Fat, 1 g Sat Fat, 303 mg Sod, 10 g Total Carb, 6 g Sugar, 4 g Fib, 2 g Prot.

Chapter 6
Beans, roots, and grains

Curried barley with apricots

Serves 6

Richly flavored dried apricots and bright green pistachio nuts are often combined, especially in Middle Eastern dishes. Here the barley is toasted to bring out its earthy flavor, while the addition of Madras curry powder adds a bit of the exotic.

¾ **cup pearl barley**

1 **tablespoon Madras curry powder**

2½ **cups water**

¾ **teaspoon salt**

2 **teaspoons olive oil**

1 **cup sliced scallions (about 4 large)**

¼ **cup pistachios, chopped**

3 **tablespoons chopped dried apricots**

1 Spray large heavy saucepan with olive oil nonstick spray and set over medium heat. Add barley and 2 teaspoons of curry powder and cook, stirring frequently, until barley is lightly toasted and mixture is fragrant, about 5 minutes.

2 Add water and ½ teaspoon of salt to saucepan and bring to boil. Reduce heat and simmer, covered, until barley is tender, about 35 minutes. Drain off any excess liquid and transfer barley to serving bowl (no need to keep warm).

3 Heat oil in same saucepan over medium heat. Add scallions and remaining 1 teaspoon curry powder and ¼ teaspoon salt and cook, stirring, until scallions are tender and mixture is fragrant, about 2 minutes.

4 Add scallion mixture, pistachios, and apricots to barley. Stir until mixed well.

 SmartPoints value per serving (about ⅔ cup): 147 Cal, 4 g Total Fat, 1 g Sat Fat, 299 mg Sod, 25 g Total Carb, 3 g Sugar, 5 g Fib, 4 g Prot.

Add this
Tossing in chopped or torn fresh mint leaves would add another layer of complexity. About ¼ cup would be the right amount.

**Curried barley
with apricots**

Lemon barley

Serves 4

1⅓ **cups water**

½   **teaspoon salt**

⅔   **cup quick-cooking barley**

2   **teaspoons olive oil**

1   **small onion, thinly sliced**

1   **zucchini, cut into ¼-inch dice**

Grated zest of 1 large lemon

¼   **teaspoon black pepper**

1 Combine water, ¼ teaspoon of salt, and barley in medium saucepan and bring to boil. Reduce heat and simmer, covered, until barley is tender, about 12 minutes.

2 Meanwhile, heat oil in medium nonstick skillet over medium heat. Add onion and zucchini and cook, stirring, until onion is golden, about 8 minutes. Stir in barley, lemon zest, pepper, and remaining ¼ teaspoon salt. Cook, stirring, until heated through, about 2 minutes longer.

2 **SmartPoints value per serving** (scant 1 cup): 74 Cal, 3 g Total Fat, 0 g Sat Fat, 299 mg Sod, 13 g Total Carb, 3 g Sugar, 2 g Fib, 2 g Prot.

Hot and smoky pink beans

Serves 8

The time it takes for dried beans to cook depends on the type of bean, how old they are, and how long they have been soaked. It's a good idea to start checking the beans for doneness after about 50 minutes of cooking time.

½ **pound dried pink beans, picked over and rinsed**

2 **teaspoons olive oil**

1 **onion, chopped**

3 **cups chicken broth**

½ **teaspoon salt**

1½ **teaspoons chipotle en adobo or to taste, minced**

1 Quick soak beans according to package directions. Drain.

2 Heat oil in medium saucepan over medium heat. Add onion and cook, stirring, until softened, about 5 minutes. Add broth and beans and bring to boil. Reduce heat to low and simmer, covered, 40 minutes. Add salt and cook, uncovered, until beans are tender and still hold their shape, 20–40 minutes longer. Stir in chipotle en adobo.

1 **SmartPoints value per serving** (about ½ cup): 127 Cal, 2 g Total Fat, 0 g Sat Fat, 436 mg Sod, 20 g Total Carb, 1 g Sugar, 4 g Fib, 8 g Prot.

Freestyle it

These delectably smoky beans would be the perfect side dish for grilled spice-rubbed skinless boneless chicken breasts, which will add 0 SmartPoints. A win-win.

White beans with roasted tomatoes

White beans with roasted tomatoes

Serves 4

This great-tasting Italian side dish can do double duty as the base for a non-vegetarian main that features a lean protein.

2	**pints red and/or yellow grape tomatoes**
1	**tablespoon extra-virgin olive oil**
1	**teaspoon dried thyme**
¾	**teaspoon kosher or coarse sea salt**
¼	**teaspoon black pepper**
1	**large garlic clove, minced**
2	**cups canned white beans, rinsed and drained (from 19-ounce can)**

Scant ¼ cup sliced fresh basil

1 Preheat oven to 400°F.

2 Toss together tomatoes, 2 teaspoons of oil, the thyme, ½ teaspoon of salt, and ⅛ teaspoon of pepper on rimmed baking sheet. Roast until tomatoes collapse, 25–35 minutes.

3 About 5 minutes before tomatoes are done, heat remaining 1 teaspoon oil in medium nonstick skillet over medium heat. Add garlic and cook, stirring, until fragrant, about 30 seconds. Add beans and remaining ¼ teaspoon salt and remaining ⅛ teaspoon pepper and cook, stirring occasionally, until heated through, about 3 minutes.

4 Spoon beans into large shallow serving bowl or plate and top with tomatoes and any accumulated juices from baking sheet. Sprinkle with basil.

1 **SmartPoints value per serving** (½ cup beans and about ½ cup tomatoes): 210 Cal, 4 g Total Fat, 1 g Sat Fat, 376 mg Sod, 34 g Total Carb, 4 g Sugar, 8 g Fib, 11 g Prot.

Spicy bulgur with carrots and harissa

Serves 4

2	**cups water**
1	**cup quick-cooking bulgur**
½	**teaspoon salt**
¼	**teaspoon black pepper**
1	**cup shredded or matchstick-cut carrots**
1	**cup frozen baby peas, thawed**
¾	**teaspoon harissa**
½	**cup chopped fresh cilantro**

1 Combine water, bulgur, salt, and pepper in large saucepan and bring to boil. Reduce heat and simmer, covered, until bulgur is tender and water is absorbed, about 10 minutes.

2 Add carrots, peas, and harissa to bulgur and cook, stirring, until carrots are just tender, about 2 minutes. Stir in cilantro.

3 **SmartPoints value per serving** (1 cup): 160 Cal, 1 g Total Fat, 0 g Sat Fat, 362 mg Sod, 34 g Total Carb, 3 g Sugar, 7 g Fib, 6 g Prot.

**Spicy bulgur with
carrots and harissa**

Whole grain tips and tricks

A grain is a whole grain when it contains all three of its parts: the outer bran layer, which contains antioxidants, vitamins, and fiber; the endosperm, the largest portion of the grain kernel that contains starchy carbohydrates, proteins, and small amounts of vitamins and minerals; and the germ, which is the "heart" of the grain and from where a new plant can sprout.

When shopping, one of the easiest ways to spot a whole grain is to look for the whole-grain stamp on the package. The yellow and black stamp features a sheath of wheat and the words 100% Whole Grain. There is also a stamp for products where at least 50% of the product is whole grain and a stamp labeled Whole Grain for products that contain less than 50% whole grain.

Another way to know if you are buying a product that is 100% whole grain is to look for these key words:

- whole grain
- whole wheat
- whole (plus name of grain)
- stoneground whole (plus name of grain)
- brown rice
- oats
- old-fashioned, rolled, quick-cook, instant oatmeal
- wheat berries

Tip: A great shortcut is to cook up a double or triple batch of grain and refrigerate in a covered container for up to 4 days. Warm the grain up a bit by letting it sit on the counter or by heating it in the microwave or in a saucepan over low heat with a bit of water added.

Tip: Short on time? Look for shelf-stable precooked brown rice in supermarkets or frozen parcooked farro in the freezer section of big box stores.

Tip: The time it takes whole grains to cook depends on three things: the freshness of the grain, the type of grain, and the pot it's cooked in.

Trick: Presoaking some grains in a specified amount of cold water for several hours or up to overnight will significantly reduce the cooking time. After soaking, add a bit more water if needed and cook the grain until tender. The cooking time will depend on the type of grain and how long it was soaked.

Trick: Add more flavor to a grain by first cooking chopped onion or a combination of onion and minced garlic in a little oil. Then add the grain and cook, stirring, until softened before adding the water—or use broth or a combination of broth and water for more flavor.

Trick: If a grain begins to stick to the bottom of the pot during cooking, take the pot off the heat and add a little water. Cover and let stand for about 5 minutes, then stir the grain from the bottom of the pot using a wooden spoon or silicone spatula.

Cooking whole grains

Method: Put the grain into a pot with the specified amount of water and bring to a boil. Reduce the heat and simmer, covered, until the grain is tender, adding a bit more liquid if needed or pouring off any excess liquid.

To 1 cup of grain	Amount of liquid	Approximate cooking time	Approximate yield
Amaranth	2 cups	25 minutes	3½ cups
Barley, pearl	3 cups	50 minutes	3½ cups
Buckwheat (kasha)	2 cups	20 minutes	4 cups
Bulgur	2 cups	10 minutes soaking time	3 cups
Couscous, whole wheat	2 cups	10 minutes soaking time	4 cups
Kamut	2½ cups	1½ hours	2½ cups
Millet	2½ cups	30 minutes	4 cups
Oats, steel-cut	4 cups	20 minutes	4 cups
Quinoa	2 cups	12 minutes	3 cups
Rice, brown (long grain)	2½ cups	30 minutes	3 cups
Rice, brown basmati	2 cups	45 minutes	4 cups
Rice, brown jasmine	2 cups	45 minutes	4 cups
Sorghum	4 cups	30 minutes	3 cups
Spelt	4 cups	soak overnight; cook 50 minutes	3 cups
Teff	3 cups	15 minutes	3 cups
Wheat berries	4 cups	soak overnight; cook 50 minutes	3 cups
Wild rice, native	2½ cups	50 minutes	4 cups
Wild rice, cultivated	2½ cups	1 hour	4 cups

Couscous with chickpeas and oranges

Serves 4

In just a few minutes you can whip up your own seasoned rice vinegar. In a cup, mix together 1 tablespoon rice vinegar, ¾ teaspoon superfine sugar, 1 teaspoon mirin or sake, and a pinch of salt until the sugar has dissolved.

1¼	**cups water**
1	**cup canned chickpeas, rinsed and drained**
¼	**teaspoon salt or to taste**
⅛	**teaspoon black pepper**
1	**cup whole wheat couscous**
2	**large navel oranges**
1	**tablespoon seasoned rice vinegar**
¼	**cup thinly sliced fresh mint**

1 Combine water, chickpeas, salt, and pepper in medium saucepan and bring to boil. Add couscous and remove saucepan from heat. Let stand, covered, until couscous is tender and water is absorbed, about 5 minutes.

2 Meanwhile, with sharp knife, peel oranges and remove white pith. Cut oranges into rounds and cut each round in quarters. Transfer couscous mixture to serving bowl; add vinegar and lightly spray with olive oil nonstick spray, tossing until coated evenly. Add oranges and mint and gently toss until combined. Serve hot, warm, or at room temperature.

5 **SmartPoints value per serving** (1¼ cups): 294 Cal, 3 g Total Fat, 0 g Sat Fat, 308 mg Sod, 59 g Total Carb, 14 g Sugar, 12 g Fib, 12 g Prot.

Add this
Stir ½ teaspoon ground cumin or to taste into the couscous mixture along with the oranges and mint.

Mashed parsnips, potatoes, and apple

Serves 6

Browned butter is special. It has a nutty flavor that can turn almost any dish from ordinary into extraordinary. Stirred into mashed parsnips, potatoes, and apple that are seasoned with salt, pepper, and fresh thyme, it becomes a delectable side.

1 **pound parsnips, peeled and cut into ½-inch slices**

1 **pound Yukon Gold potatoes, peeled and cut into ¾-inch chunks**

1 **large McIntosh apple, peeled, cored, and cut into ¾-inch chunks**

1 **cup water**

2 **tablespoons unsalted butter**

½ **teaspoon chopped fresh thyme**

1 **teaspoon salt**

⅛ **teaspoon black pepper**

1 Combine parsnips, potatoes, apple, and water in large saucepan and set over medium heat. Cook, covered, stirring occasionally, until vegetables have softened, about 20 minutes.

2 Meanwhile, melt butter in small nonstick skillet over medium heat and cook until butter starts to foam. Swirl pan and cook until foam subsides and milk solids turn brown. Pour over parsnip mixture.

3 With potato masher, mash parsnip mixture until it forms coarse puree. Stir in thyme, salt, and pepper. Stir in a bit of water if mixture seems dry, reheating over low heat if needed before serving.

5 **SmartPoints value per serving** (about ¾ cup): 161 Cal, 4 g Total Fat, 3 g Sat Fat, 409 mg Sod, 30 g Total Carb, 8 g Sugar, 6 g Fib, 2 g Prot.

Crispy
Hasselback
potatoes

Crispy Hasselback potatoes

Serves 4

This company-perfect potato dish is named after Stockholm's historic Hasselbacken Hotel, but it is also known as accordion potatoes in the U.S.

4 **(5-ounce) Yukon Gold potatoes, scrubbed**

2 **teaspoons olive oil**

1 **large garlic clove, minced**

½ **teaspoon salt**

¼ **teaspoon black pepper**

Maldon sea salt (optional)

1 Preheat oven to 425°F. Line small rimmed baking sheet with sheet of parchment paper.

2 Peel potatoes, leaving lengthwise strip of skin on one long side of each potato. Place potatoes, skin-side down, on cutting board. With thin sharp knife, cut each potato crosswise into ⅛-inch slices, stopping about ¼ inch from bottom.

3 Drizzle potatoes with oil, gently separating slices so oil can seep down and coat potatoes. Sprinkle with garlic, salt, and pepper, separating slices to ensure seasoning coats every slice.

4 Place potatoes, skin-side down, on prepared baking sheet and bake until potatoes are browned and tender, about 50 minutes. Sprinkle with Maldon salt, if using.

4 **SmartPoints value per serving** (1 potato): 119 Cal, 2 g Total Fat, 0 g Sat Fat, 313 mg Sod, 22 g Total Carb, 2 g Sugar, 3 g Fib, 2 g Prot.

Add this
Add some finely minced fresh thyme to the potatoes along with garlic.

Cast-iron skillet potato kugel

Serves 8

Gluten-free potato starch helps make this kugel (aka pudding) extra light. Potato starch is not the same as potato flour. Potato starch is made from the starch of the potato and is flavorless, while potato flour is made from the flesh.

1	onion, cut into chunks
2	pounds small russet potatoes, peeled
2	large eggs, lightly beaten
¼	cup potato starch
1½	teaspoons kosher salt
¼	teaspoon black pepper
2	tablespoons olive oil

1 Preheat oven to 350°F.

2 Finely chop onion in food processor. Transfer to large bowl. To create long shreds, trim potatoes so they fit horizontally in feed tube. With shredding blade in place, shred potatoes and add to onion. Add eggs, potato starch, salt, and pepper and stir until mixed well.

3 Heat oil in 10-inch cast-iron or other heavy ovenproof skillet over medium-high heat until very hot. Add potato mixture (it should sizzle), spreading to form even layer, twisting potato shreds on top to form decorative pattern. Spray with olive oil nonstick spray.

4 Bake until potatoes are golden and crisp on top and tender when knife is inserted, about 1 hour 10 minutes.

5 Cut kugel into 8 wedges and sprinkle with additional salt and pepper if desired.

 SmartPoints value per serving (1 wedge): 163 Cal, 5 g Total Fat, 1 g Sat Fat, 386 mg Sod, 27 g Total Carb, 1 g Sugar, 2 g Fib, 4 g Prot.

Add this
The combination of potatoes and herbs are a perfect marriage. Add 2 teaspoons of chopped fresh thyme or rosemary to the potatoes along with the eggs in step 2.

Cheddar potato "fries"

Serves 4

Crisp on the outside and oh-so-tender on the inside are the hallmarks of great fries. To ensure those delectable qualities, keep the potatoes separated on the baking sheet so the heat of the oven touches every inch of the potatoes.

2   **(9-ounce) russet potatoes**

¼   **teaspoon salt**

¼   **teaspoon black pepper**

½   **cup shredded reduced-fat Cheddar cheese**

1 Preheat oven to 400°F. Line large rimmed baking sheet with silicone baking mat or sheet of parchment paper.

2 Peel potatoes and cut into ¼-inch-thick matchstick strips (you should have about 52 total). Put on prepared baking sheet. Spray potatoes with nonstick spray and sprinkle with salt and pepper, tossing to coat evenly. Spread potatoes to form even layer, making sure they do not overlap or touch.

3 Bake potatoes 20 minutes. Turn fries over and spread out. Bake until golden brown, about 20 minutes longer. Gather fries together and sprinkle with Cheddar. Bake until cheese has melted, about 5 minutes longer. Transfer fries with baking sheet to wire rack and let cool slightly before serving.

4   **SmartPoints value per serving** (about 13 "fries"): 142 Cal, 3 g Total Fat, 2 g Sat Fat, 240 mg Sod, 23 g Total Carb, 1 g Sugar, 3 g Fib, 6 g Prot.

German-style potato-sauerkraut salad

Serves 6

Potato salad, known as *kartoffelsalat* in Germany, is usually served warm. It sometimes contains bold-flavored mustard to give it a little punch, which would be a great addition to our salad.

8	**small red potatoes, scrubbed**
1	**(¼-pound) piece skinless smoked turkey breast, cut into ½-inch dice**
2	**scallions, thinly sliced**
1	**tablespoon extra-virgin olive oil**
1–1½	**teaspoons caraway seeds, crushed (optional)**
½	**teaspoon salt**
¼	**teaspoon black pepper**
12	**ounces fresh sauerkraut (bagged or jarred), undrained (about 2 cups), at room temperature**

1 Combine potatoes with enough salted water to cover by 1 inch in small saucepan and bring to boil. Reduce heat and simmer until potatoes are fork-tender, about 12 minutes. Drain and let cool about 5 minutes. Cut warm potatoes in quarters.

2 Combine potatoes, turkey, scallions, oil, caraway seeds (if using), salt, and pepper in serving bowl. Add sauerkraut and gently toss until combined.

 SmartPoints value per serving (⅔ cup): 213 Cal, 3 g Total Fat, 1 g Sat Fat, 700 mg Sod, 40 g Total Carb, 4 g Sugar, 6 g Fib, 8 g Prot.

German-style
potato-sauerkraut salad

**Smashed potatoes
with lemon salt**

Smashed potatoes with lemon salt

Serves 4

You can also make this delicious potato dish with smaller potatoes. Use 8 (2-ounce) potatoes, and keep in mind that the cooking time will be reduced to about 12 minutes.

4	(¼-pound) red or yellow potatoes, scrubbed
¾	teaspoon kosher or coarse sea salt
½	teaspoon grated lemon zest
2	teaspoons extra-virgin olive oil
1	large garlic clove, thinly sliced
1	tablespoon chopped fresh parsley

1 Combine potatoes with enough salted water to cover by 1 inch in medium saucepan and bring to boil. Reduce heat and simmer, covered, until potatoes are fork-tender, about 25 minutes. Drain potatoes and let cool about 5 minutes.

2 Meanwhile combine salt and lemon zest in cup, rubbing them together with fingers to bring out lemon oil. Set aside.

3 Put potatoes on cutting board and gently press down on each potato with palm of hand or pancake spatula to flatten slightly (the edges of potatoes will split).

4 Combine oil and garlic in large nonstick skillet and set over medium heat. Cook, stirring, until garlic is lightly toasted, about 1 minute. With slotted spoon, lift out garlic and transfer to separate cup.

5 Add potatoes to skillet and cook over medium-high heat until browned and crisp on bottom, about 5 minutes. With small spatula, gently turn potatoes over and cook until second side is browned and crisp, about 5 minutes longer. Transfer potatoes to small platter and sprinkle with lemon salt, garlic chips, and parsley.

(3) **SmartPoints value per serving** (1 potato): 101 Cal, 2 g Total Fat, 0 g Sat Fat, 383 mg Sod, 18 g Total Carb, 1 g Sugar, 2 g Fib, 2 g Prot.

Classic French potato salad

Serves 6

It's pure genius tossing still-warm cooked potatoes with a liquid such as stock or vinegar. This technique makes it easy for the potatoes to absorb it, flavoring them all the way through.

6	(¼-pound) Yukon Gold potatoes, peeled
2	tablespoons champagne vinegar
⅓–½	cup chopped fresh herbs, such as parsley, dill, and basil
2	scallions, finely chopped
1	large shallot, finely chopped (⅓ cup)
2	tablespoons extra-virgin olive oil
¾	teaspoon salt
¼	teaspoon black pepper or to taste

1 Combine potatoes with enough salted water to cover by 1 inch in medium saucepan and bring to boil. Reduce heat and simmer, covered, until potatoes are tender, about 20 minutes. Drain and let cool about 5 minutes. Cut potatoes into ¾-inch chunks and transfer to serving bowl.

2 Sprinkle vinegar over warm potatoes and gently toss to coat. Let stand 5 minutes, tossing once or twice. Add herbs, scallions, shallot, oil, salt, and pepper and gently toss until mixed well. Let stand, about 10 minutes. Serve warm or at room temperature.

 SmartPoints value per serving (generous ¾ cup): 128 Cal, 5 g Total Fat, 1 g Sat Fat, 312 mg Sod, 20 g Total Carb, 2 g Sugar, 3 g Fib, 2 g Prot.

Classic French potato salad

Savory spinach-Parmesan oats

Serves 4

On trend and super satisfying is the best way to describe this breakfast dish. Since it takes less than 20 minutes to prepare, it can likely fit into your weekday breakfast routine.

2	scallions, thinly sliced
3½	cups water
2	cups old-fashioned (rolled) oats
½	teaspoon salt
2	cups lightly packed baby spinach
¼	teaspoon black pepper
¼	cup grated Parmesan cheese
2	teaspoons extra-virgin olive oil

1 Spray 8-cup glass measure or microwavable bowl with nonstick spray. Add scallions and microwave on High until softened, about 1 minute.

2 Add water, oats, and salt to scallions. Cover with piece of microwavable plastic wrap with one side folded back to vent or cover with microwavable plate. Microwave on High until oats have thickened, about 8 minutes, stirring about every minute.

3 Stir spinach and pepper into oat mixture. Let stand, covered, until spinach has wilted, about 1 minute. Spoon evenly into 4 bowls; sprinkle with Parmesan and drizzle with oil.

6 **SmartPoints value per serving** (1 cup oatmeal, 1 tablespoon Parmesan, and ½ teaspoon olive oil): 213 Cal, 7 g Total Fat, 2 g Sat Fat, 423 mg Sod, 29 g Total Carb, 1 g Sugar, 5 g Fib, 9 g Prot.

Red quinoa with parsley and pine nuts

Serves 6

Quinoa (KEEN-wah) has risen to star power. High in protein and fiber, it has a nutty flavor and invitingly chewy texture. Because its natural outer coating has a bitter flavor, always rinse quinoa unless it says "prerinsed" on the package.

2	**cups water**
1	**cup red quinoa**
½	**teaspoon salt or to taste**
1½	**tablespoons white wine vinegar**
2	**teaspoons extra-virgin olive oil**
¼	**teaspoon black pepper**
⅓	**cup chopped fresh flat-leaf parsley**
3	**tablespoons pine nuts, toasted**

1 Bring water to boil in small saucepan; stir in quinoa and salt. Reduce heat and simmer, covered, until water is absorbed and quinoa is tender, about 15 minutes. Remove saucepan from heat and let stand 5 minutes; fluff quinoa with fork.

2 Whisk together vinegar, oil, and pepper in serving bowl. Add quinoa, parsley, and pine nuts and toss until mixed well. Taste and season with additional salt, if desired.

 SmartPoints value per serving (generous ½ cup): 144 Cal, 5 g Total Fat, 1 g Sat Fat, 200 mg Sod, 19 g Total Carb, 0 g Sugar, 2 g Fib, 5 g Prot.

Polenta with spinach and cheese

Polenta with spinach and cheese

Serves 4

Comfort in a bowl describes this dish. Quick-cooking polenta gets extra flavor by being whisked into chicken broth instead of water. If you happen to have homemade stock in your freezer, use it here. Get the most enjoyment by eating this with a spoon!

2	**cups reduced-sodium chicken broth**
½	**cup instant polenta**
4	**cups lightly packed baby spinach**
¼	**teaspoon salt**
¼	**teaspoon black pepper**
¼	**cup grated Parmesan cheese**

1 Bring broth to boil in medium saucepan over medium-high heat. Whisk in polenta in thin, steady stream. Stir in spinach, salt, and pepper.

2 Reduce heat to medium-low and cook, stirring occasionally, until polenta has thickened, about 4 minutes. Remove saucepan from heat and stir in Parmesan. Serve immediately.

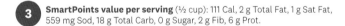

3 **SmartPoints value per serving** (½ cup): 111 Cal, 2 g Total Fat, 1 g Sat Fat, 559 mg Sod, 18 g Total Carb, 0 g Sugar, 2 g Fib, 6 g Prot.

The real deal fried rice

Serves 6

What makes this fried rice authentic is the omission of soy sauce, which is the typical way to serve it in China. That said, there is nothing wrong with serving soy sauce at the table.

1 teaspoon canola or peanut oil

1 (6-ounce) piece lean ham steak, diced

4 various color mini sweet peppers, diced (1 cup)

5 scallions, sliced (green and white parts separated)

2 (8½-ounce) pouches ready-to-serve basmati rice

¼ cup water

½ teaspoon salt

⅛ teaspoon black pepper

2 large eggs, beaten

1 Heat oil in large nonstick skillet over high heat. Add ham, sweet peppers, and white part of scallions and cook, stirring occasionally, until peppers are tender and lightly colored in spots, about 6 minutes.

2 Add rice, water, salt, and black pepper to skillet and cook, breaking up rice and scraping bottom of skillet to lift up any browned bits, until rice is hot, about 3 minutes.

3 Push rice mixture to one side of skillet and pour beaten eggs into empty side of skillet. Cook until eggs begin to set on bottom, about 1 minute; stir eggs and cook until set, breaking them up, 2 minutes longer. Stir eggs and green part of scallions into rice mixture.

5 **SmartPoints value per serving** (⅔ cup): 227 Cal, 7 g Total Fat, 1 g Sat Fat, 673 mg Sod, 30 g Total Carb, 1 g Sugar, 3 g Fib, 11 g Prot.

**The real deal
fried rice**

Coconut-cardamom basmati rice

Serves 6

1	cup water
1	cup brown basmati rice
1	cup light (low-fat) coconut milk
½	teaspoon ground cardamom
½	teaspoon salt
⅛	teaspoon black pepper

Bring water to boil in medium saucepan. Add rice, coconut milk, cardamom, salt, and pepper and return to boil. Reduce heat and simmer, covered, until rice is tender and liquid is absorbed, about 40 minutes.

 SmartPoints value per serving (½ cup): 141 Cal, 3 g Total Fat, 2 g Sat Fat, 197 mg Sod, 26 g Total Carb, 0 g Sugar, 0 g Fib, 2 g Prot.

Freestyle it

This side dish, fragrant from basmati rice and richly flavored from coconut milk, would pair well with broiled or grilled salt and pepper seasoned shrimp for no additional SmartPoints.

Roasted garlic–herb bread

Serves 6

Our irresistible roasted garlic-Parmesan mixture is also great spooned over steamed green beans, spread over grilled chicken or salmon steaks, or used as a topping for steamed baby potatoes.

1	**head garlic**
¼	**cup grated Parmesan cheese**
¾	**teaspoon dried Italian seasoning**
½	**(12-ounce) whole-grain or whole wheat baguette, sliced lengthwise in half**

1 Preheat oven to 375°F.

2 Cut head of garlic crosswise in half. Lightly spray all over with olive oil nonstick spray and tightly wrap in sheet of foil. Place foil package directly on oven rack and roast until garlic is very tender when squeezed, about 1 hour.

3 When cool enough to handle, unwrap garlic and squeeze out pulp from each clove into small bowl. Add Parmesan and Italian seasoning, mashing mixture with fork until smooth and combined.

4 Preheat broiler.

5 Spread garlic-Parmesan mixture over cut sides of bread. Place bread, cut-side up, on broiler rack and broil 5 inches from heat until browned in spots and heated through, about 2 minutes. Cut bread into 12 pieces.

3 **SmartPoints value per serving** (2 pieces): 107 Cal, 2 g Total Fat, 1 g Sat Fat, 208 mg Sod, 17 g Total Carb, 1 g Sugar, 2 g Fib, 6 g Prot.

Mixed rice pilaf with orange

Serves 6

1 tablespoon olive oil

1 small onion, chopped

1 celery stalk, cut into small dice

1½ cups water

Grated zest and juice of 1 orange

½ teaspoon salt

¼ teaspoon black pepper

1 cup brown and wild rice blend

¼ cup dried currants

1 Heat oil in medium saucepan over medium heat. Add onion and celery and cook, stirring, until softened, about 5 minutes. Add water, ¼ cup of orange juice (save remaining juice for another use), the salt, and pepper and bring to boil. Stir in rice. Reduce heat and simmer, covered, until rice is tender and liquid is absorbed, about 45 minutes, sprinkling currants on top during last 5 minutes of cooking.

2 Remove saucepan from heat and let stand, covered, 10 minutes. Fluff rice with fork and stir in orange zest. Transfer to serving bowl.

3 **SmartPoints value per serving** (about ⅔ cup): 88 Cal, 3 g Total Fat, 0 g Sat Fat, 312 mg Sod, 15 g Total Carb, 7 g Sugar, 2 g Fib, 2 g Prot.

**Mixed rice pilaf
with orange**

Chapter 7
Sweet nothings

Plum crostata

Plum crostata

Serves 8

4	large plums (about 1½ pounds), halved, pitted, and cut into thin wedges
⅓	cup plus 1 tablespoon sugar
1½	tablespoons all-purpose flour
¼	teaspoon ground cinnamon or ⅛ teaspoon freshly grated nutmeg
1	refrigerated piecrust (from 14.1-ounce) package, softened according to package directions

1 Preheat oven to 400°F. Line large baking sheet with sheet of heavy foil or parchment paper; lightly spray with nonstick spray.

2 To make filling, toss together plums, ⅓ cup of sugar, the flour, and cinnamon in medium bowl.

3 On lightly floured work surface with floured rolling pin, roll piecrust into 13-inch round. Fold piecrust in quarters; transfer to prepared baking sheet and gently unfold being careful not to stretch dough.

4 Pile plum mixture on piecrust leaving 1½- to 2-inch border. Scatter any sugar mixture remaining in bowl over plums. Fold edge of piecrust over filling, pleating it as you go. Sprinkle remaining 1 tablespoon sugar over plums. Bake until filling is bubbly and crust is golden, about 45 minutes. Let cool on baking sheet on wire rack.

 SmartPoints value per serving (⅛ of crostata): 210 Cal, 8 g Total Fat, 3 g Sat Fat, 117 mg Sod, 36 g Total Carb, 19 g Sugar, 2 g Fib, 2 g Prot.

Baked almond crisp-topped peaches

Serves 8

An old-fashioned crisp is a simple country-style dessert where fruit is topped with a mix of flour, brown sugar, and butter and baked. We used halved peaches because it's even easier to coat them with our topping that includes almonds and oats for crunch.

4	**(6-ounce) firm-ripe peaches, halved and pitted**
¼	**cup whole almonds**
¼	**cup packed light brown sugar**
⅛	**teaspoon salt**
2	**tablespoons cold unsalted butter, cut into pieces**
⅓	**cup old-fashioned (rolled) oats**

1 Preheat oven to 375°F.

2 Place peaches, cut-side up, in small shallow baking dish that has been sprayed with nonstick spray. Combine almonds, brown sugar, and salt in food processor and pulse until almonds are coarsely chopped. Add butter and pulse until mixture is evenly moistened and forms small clumps; add oats and pulse just until mixed. Spoon about 3 tablespoons of almond mixture into center of each peach, pressing lightly to cover peaches.

3 Bake until topping is golden brown and crisp and peaches are tender when pierced with knife but still hold their shape, about 40 minutes. Transfer peaches to wire rack and let cool about 10 minutes. Serve warm or at room temperature.

4 **SmartPoints value per serving** (½ stuffed peach): 115 Cal, 5 g Total Fat, 2 g Sat Fat, 75 mg Sod, 18 g Total Carb, 14 g Sugar, 2 g Fib, 2 g Prot.

Chocolate-orange mousse

Serves 8

If you accidentally over-whisk the chocolate mixture and it turns grainy, simply remelt it over very low heat and whisk again.

2 **small oranges**

½ **cup refrigerated liquid egg whites**

¼ **cup confectioners' sugar**

⅔ **cup bittersweet chocolate chips**

⅓ **cup boiling water**

1 **(6-ounce) container orange crème low-fat whipped or custard-style yogurt**

1 Grate ½ teaspoon zest from 1 orange; reserve. Section both oranges and cut sections crosswise in half; refrigerate if leaving out for more than 2 hours.

2 With electric mixer on low speed, beat egg whites and confectioners' sugar in large bowl until sugar has dissolved. Increase speed to medium-high and beat until stiff peaks form when beaters are lifted, about 10 minutes, scraping down side of bowl once or twice.

3 Put chocolate chips in medium bowl and pour boiling water over. Wait about 30 seconds, then stir until chocolate is melted and mixture is smooth. Place bowl of chocolate over larger bowl filled with ice water. Whisk constantly just until chocolate is thickened to consistency of soft pudding, 2–3 minutes.

4 Immediately remove whipped chocolate from ice water and gently fold in yogurt, orange zest, and large spoonful of beaten whites to lighten mixture. Fold in remaining whites just until no longer visible. Spoon mousse into 8 dessert glasses dividing evenly. Refrigerate until set, about 2 hours or up to 6 hours.

5 To serve, top each serving of mousse with orange sections.

 SmartPoints value per serving (½ cup mousse and about 3 orange sections): 149 Cal, 6 g Total Fat, 4 g Sat Fat, 40 mg Sod, 22 g Total Carb, 18 g Sugar, 2 g Fib, 4 g Prot.

Red wine-poached pears

Serves 6

Wine-poached pears are as classic and elegant as a simple black dress that never goes out of style. In this recipe, the pears are poached in a flavorful red-wine mixture until tender enough to be easily pierced with a paring knife.

1½	**cups dry red wine, such as merlot or cabernet sauvignon**
1	**cup water**
¼	**cup sugar**
2	**(3-inch) strips lemon zest, removed with vegetable peeler**
1	**(3-inch) cinnamon stick**
6	**(5-ounce) firm-ripe Bartlett or Bosc pears with stems**

1 Combine wine, water, sugar, lemon zest, and cinnamon stick in saucepan just large enough to hold pears and set over medium heat. Cook, stirring occasionally, until sugar has dissolved. Remove saucepan from heat.

2 Meanwhile, peel pears leaving stems intact. Add pears to wine mixture and bring to boil. Reduce heat to low and simmer, covered, turning pears occasionally, until pears are evenly colored and tender when pierced with knife, about 30 minutes.

3 With slotted spoon, transfer pears to large bowl. Pour poaching liquid through fine sieve set over medium saucepan and bring to boil. Cook until syrupy and reduced to about ½ cup, about 20 minutes. Let cool to room temperature.

4 Transfer pears to large zip-close plastic bag and add cooled syrup. Squeeze out most of air and seal bag. Gently turn bag to coat pears. Put bag with pears in large bowl and refrigerate at least overnight or up to 4 days, turning bag several times.

5 To serve, place pears on dessert plates and spoon syrup over.

 SmartPoints value per serving (1 pear and about 1 tablespoon syrup): 195 Cal, 0 g Total Fat, 0 g Sat Fat, 5 mg Sod, 37 g Total Carb, 26 g Sugar, 6 g Fib, 1 g Prot.

Red wine–poached pears

Matcha-chocolate meringue bark

Serves 16

Don't be daunted by the idea of making a meringue. It's nothing more than egg whites beaten with sugar—your mixer does all the work. The only thing to keep in mind is that meringue should be made on a day when the humidity is low or it won't crisp.

1	**tablespoon water**
2	**teaspoons matcha (green tea powder)**
5	**large egg whites, at room temperature**
½	**cup superfine sugar**
2	**tablespoons mini semisweet chocolate chips**
4	**teaspoons toasted sesame seeds**

1 Preheat oven to 250°F. Line large rimmed baking sheet with sheet of parchment paper.

2 Stir together water and matcha in cup. With electric mixer on medium speed, beat egg whites in large bowl until soft peaks form when beaters are lifted. Beat in sugar, 1 tablespoon at a time, until stiff, glossy peaks form. Beat in matcha mixture until meringue is pale green, about 1 minute longer.

3 Place dab of meringue on underside of each corner of parchment to help keep parchment in place. Pile meringue on parchment and spread with offset spatula to form 9 x 12-inch rectangle (about ¾ inch thick). Sprinkle chocolate chips and sesame seeds evenly over meringue.

4 Bake until meringue looks dry and set but is slightly soft in center when gently pressed, about 2½ hours. Turn off oven and leave meringue in oven until meringue is firm and crisp, at least 4 hours or up to overnight. (Meringue will turn light beige.)

5 Turn meringue bark with parchment over and carefully peel off parchment. Turn meringue bark right-side up. Using serrated knife, gently cut into 16 pieces. The bark is best served on the day it is prepared.

2 **SmartPoints value per serving** (1 piece): 43 Cal, 1 g Total Fat, 0 g Sat Fat, 17 mg Sod, 8 g Total Carb, 7 g Sugar, 1 g Fib, 1 g Prot.

Banana-chocolate chip "ice cream"

Serves 4

4   **ripe large bananas**
½   **teaspoon vanilla extract**
¼   **cup mini semisweet chocolate chips**
2   **tablespoons sliced almonds, toasted**

1 Peel bananas and cut into 1-inch chunks. Place in large zip-close plastic bag. Squeeze out air and seal bag. Place in freezer until bananas are frozen solid, at least 3 hours or up to overnight.

2 Put frozen bananas in food processor and puree, scraping down side of food processor with rubber spatula once or twice. Add vanilla and pulse until mixed. Transfer to medium bowl and stir in chocolate chips.

3 Scoop ice cream into 4 dessert dishes and sprinkle with almonds. Or cover and freeze up to 1 day, leaving ice cream out on counter about 10 minutes for easier scooping.

3 **SmartPoints value per serving** (½ cup "ice cream" and 1½ teaspoons almonds): 191 Cal, 5 g Total Fat, 2 g Sat Fat, 2 mg Sod, 39 g Total Carb, 21 g Sugar, 5 g Fib, 3 g Prot.

**Vanilla bean
panna cotta**

Vanilla bean panna cotta

Serves 4

This delectable light Italian dessert is simply an eggless custard. Our recipe is easily doubled, making it perfect for dinner parties and occasions.

1¼	teaspoons unflavored gelatin
2	tablespoons cold water
1	vanilla bean, split or ¾ teaspoon vanilla extract
1	cup low-fat buttermilk
¾	cup half-and-half
¼	cup sugar

1 Lightly spray 4 (5-ounce) ramekins, (6-ounce) custard cups, or wineglasses with nonstick spray.

2 Sprinkle gelatin over water in cup. Let stand until gelatin has softened, about 5 minutes.

3 Meanwhile, with edge of small knife, split vanilla-bean pod and scrape out seeds reserving both pod and seeds.

4 Combine buttermilk, half-and-half, sugar, and vanilla pod and seeds in small saucepan and set over medium heat. Cook, whisking occasionally, until mixture is hot and sugar has dissolved, 4–5 minutes. Remove saucepan from heat and add gelatin mixture, whisking until it has completely dissolved. Pour panna cotta through sieve set over medium bowl or glass measure. Stir in vanilla extract, if using.

5 Divide custard mixture evenly among prepared ramekins. Refrigerate until panna cotta is chilled and set, at least 4 hours or up to 1 day.

 SmartPoints value per serving (1 panna cotta): 133 Cal, 5 g Total Fat, 4 g Sat Fat, 145 mg Sod, 18 g Total Carb, 17 g Sugar, 0 g Fib, 4 g Prot.

Freestyle it
Top each panna cotta with a few fresh raspberries for no additional SmartPoints.

**Hibiscus granita
with grilled mango**

Hibiscus granita with grilled mango

Serves 4

Did you know that a baking pan is made of metal while a baking dish is glass or ceramic? We used a metal baking pan in this recipe, as it speeds up the freezing process.

6	hibiscus-berry tea bags
1½	cups boiling water
1	lime, halved
1½	cups ice water
3	tablespoons light agave nectar
2	firm-ripe mangoes

1 Place tea bags in 1-quart glass measure. Add boiling water and steep 30 minutes.

2 Meanwhile, squeeze juice from one half of lime and set aside; cut remaining half into 4 wedges.

3 Remove tea bags and squeeze out liquid; discard bags. Add ice water, lime juice, and agave nectar to tea, stirring until blended. Pour tea mixture into 8-inch square baking pan. Cover pan with foil and freeze until mixture is frozen along edges but still slushy in center, about 2 hours. With fork, scrape icy edges in toward center. Repeat every 30 minutes until granita is semifirm and granular.

4 Place mango on cutting board and cut off a thick slice on one side of the pit. Repeat on other side. With tip of knife, lightly score flesh.

5 Meanwhile, set ridged grill pan over medium heat until hot. Lightly spray cut sides of mango with nonstick spray. Place mango, cut-side down, in grill pan and cook, turning once, until mango is tender and nicely marked, about 4 minutes.

6 To serve, with fork, scrape granita transferring ice shards to 4 dessert dishes. Place mango and lime wedges alongside.

3 **SmartPoints value per serving** (about ⅔ cup granita and ½ mango): 152 Cal, 1 g Total Fat, 0 g Sat Fat, 5 mg Sod, 39 g Total Carb, 34 g Sugar, 4 g Fib, 2 g Prot.

**Polenta "pizza"
margherita,
page 116**

**Green sauce–
marinated shrimp,
page 91**

Recipes by SmartPoints value

0 SmartPoints
South-of-the-border salad, 71
Whole roasted tandoori cauliflower, 131

1 SmartPoints
Braised red cabbage and pears, 125
Carrot-horseradish puree, 128
Cauliflower with lemon and cumin, 129
Cheesy kale crisps, 45
Chicken kebabs with pineapple, 97
Chilaquiles bake, 16
Chunky cucumber-yogurt salad, 72
"Creamed" corn, 134
Double orange–mint salad, 75
Fresh corn-basil soup, 52
Greek tzatziki dip, 37
Green sauce–marinated shrimp, 91
Grilled zucchini with feta and lemon, 147
Hot and smoky pink beans, 155
Lemony fennel and radicchio, 137
Marinated tofu and vegetable kebabs, 119
Miso-glazed salmon, 84
Miso soup with tofu and scallions, 53
Mustardy deviled eggs, 33
North African red lentil soup, 54
Roasted acorn squash with thyme, 143
Root vegetable chips, 44
Rosemary-roasted radishes, 141
Seared scallops with edamame puree, 89
Stir-fried garlic spinach, 142
Sumac-dusted onion and chickpeas, 78
Thai egg drop soup, 61
Tomato and garlic–stuffed peppers, 144
Very French grated carrot salad, 127
White beans with roasted tomatoes, 157

2 SmartPoints
Baked eggs in tomatoes florentine, 8
Baked tilapia with grapes and olives, 85
Catfish with salsa and olives, 88
Chickpea-broccoli soup, 63
Crab salad–topped cucumber, 36
Flounder in crazy water, 87
Grilled Parmesan corn on the cob, 132
Lemon and pecorino popcorn, 47
Lemon barley, 154
Matcha-chocolate meringue bark, 192
Parmesan-pepper green bean "fries," 43
Pea soup with smoked salmon, 59
Peas with crispy prosciutto, 139
Provençal tomato tart, 38
Quick-cook fresh tomato sauce, 146
Sesame broccoli, 124
Skinny breakfast sausages and eggs, 12
Soba noodle–mushroom soup, 57
Spicy blue cheese–chicken burgers, 95
Three-vegetable tian, 149

3 SmartPoints
Bacon and Cheddar–coddled eggs, 13
Banana–chocolate chip "ice cream," 193
Chicken with black bean sauce, 94
Coconut-cucumber splash, 31
Coconut-cumin green beans, 135
Fresh pea salad with bacon, 74
Fresh salmon-ginger burgers, 82
Greek-style breakfast pitas, 11
Gruyère and asparagus frittata, 3
Hearty turkey-barley stew, 102
Hibiscus granita with grilled mango, 197
Lotsa fruit spritzers, 32
Mixed rice pilaf with orange, 182
Niçoise-inspired tuna salad, 67
Overstuffed western omelette, 4
Polenta with spinach and cheese, 177
Roasted Brussels sprouts with walnuts, 122
Roasted garlic–herb bread, 181
Romaine and sun-dried tomato salad, 70
Silky chickpea soup with cumin, 50
Simple potato-leek soup, 60
Smashed potatoes with lemon salt, 171
Spicy bulgur with carrots and harissa, 158
Stir-fried tofu with scallions, 115

4 SmartPoints

5 SmartPoints

6 SmartPoints

7 SmartPoints

8 SmartPoints

9 SmartPoints

Index

Simply 5 Cookbook

120 brilliantly flavored dishes with 5 ingredients or less

WW Publishing Group

Managing Editor: Valeria Bloom

Food Editor: Eileen Runyan

Writer and Project Editor: Deborah Mintcheff

Contributing Editors: Lisa Chernick,
Leslie Fink, MS, RD

Nutrition Consultant: Laureen Jean Leyden

Recipe Developers: Terry Grieco Kenny,
Frank Melodia, Angela Nilsen

Creative Director: Ed Melnitsky

Design Director: Daniela A. Hritcu

Designers: Arlene Lappen, Rebecca Kollmer

Production Manager: Alan Biederman

Photo Director: Marybeth Dulany

Photographer: Jennifer Causey

Food Stylist: Rebecca Jurkevich

Prop Stylist: Bette Blau

© Copyright 2018 WW International, Inc.

Nothing may be reprinted in whole or in part without permission from the publisher. Editorial and art produced by W/W Twentyfirst Corp., 675 Avenue of the Americas, New York, NY 10010.

The WW Coin Logo, SmartPoints, Points, and WW Freestyle logo are trademarks of WW International, Inc.

SKU #61009
Printed in China

Front cover:
Provençal tomato tart, page 38